A-Level Year 1 & AS

Physics

Exam Board: AQA

Physics is great, isn't it? No awkward living things to worry about, just atoms and waves and forces and formulas and equations... we could wax lyrical for hours.

But it's definitely not easy, which is why you'll love this CGP book. It explains everything you need to know for the AQA AS course (and Year 1 of A-Level) with the clearest study notes around — and there are plenty of exam-style questions to test your skills.

And if you find paper a bit primitive, never fear — there's a free Online Edition too. You can read it on your PC, Mac or tablet, and it's all thanks to Physics. Lovely Physics.

How to access your free Online Edition

This book includes a free Online Edition to read on your PC, Mac or tablet.
You'll just need to go to **cgpbooks.co.uk/extras** and enter this code:

3674 8289 3999 2888

By the way, this code only works for one person. If somebody else has used this book before you, they might have already claimed the Online Edition.

A-Level revision? It has to be CGP!

Published by CGP

Editors:
Emily Garrett, Sharon Keeley-Holden, Andy Park, Ethan Starmer-Jones, Hannah Taylor and Charlotte Whiteley.

Contributors:
Tony Alldridge, Jane Cartwright, Peter Cecil, Barbara Mascetti, John Myers, Oliver Rigg, Frances Rooney and Andy Williams.

With thanks to Mark Edwards and Duncan Lindsay for the proofreading.
With thanks to Jan Greenway for the copyright research.

ISBN: 978 1 78908 030 8

Contents

Atomic Structure

"So what did you do today, Johnny?" "Particle physics, Mum." "How nice dear — done with times tables then?"
*Yeah, well, it's not exactly the **easiest** topic in the world, but it's a darn sight more interesting than biology.*

Atoms are made up of Protons, Neutrons and Electrons

Inside **every atom**, there's a **nucleus** containing **protons** and **neutrons**.
Protons and **neutrons** are both known as **nucleons**. **Orbiting** this core are the **electrons**.
This is the **nuclear model** of the atom.

The diagram shows **neutral oxygen**, with **eight protons** and **eight electrons**.

The nucleus — containing
protons and neutrons

The electrons in orbit
around the nucleus

Tom dreamt of
becoming a nuclear
model when he grew up.

The particles in an atom have different **properties**. Their charges and masses are so **tiny**
that it's often easier to talk about their **relative charge** and **relative mass**.

> You need to learn
> the values in the
> orange columns —
> you won't be given
> them in the exam.

Particle	Charge (coulombs, C)	Mass (kg)	Relative Charge	Relative Mass
Proton	$+1.60 \times 10^{-19}$	1.67×10^{-27}	$+1$	1
Neutron	0	1.67×10^{-27}	0	1
Electron	-1.60×10^{-19}	9.11×10^{-31}	-1	0.0005

The Proton Number is the Number of Protons in the Nucleus

No... really.

The **proton number** is sometimes called the **atomic number**, and has the **symbol Z**
(I'm sure it makes sense to someone). **Z** is just the **number of protons** in the nucleus.

It's the **proton number** that **defines** the element — **no two elements** will have the **same** number of protons.

In a **neutral atom**, the number of **electrons equals** the number of **protons**.
The element's **reactions** and **chemical behaviour** depend on the number of **electrons**.
So the **proton number** tells you a lot about its **chemical properties**.

> A particle with a different
> number of electrons to
> protons is called an ion.

The Nucleon Number is the Total Number of Protons and Neutrons

The **nucleon number** is also called the **mass number**, and has the **symbol A** (*shrug*).
It tells you how many **protons** and **neutrons** are in the nucleus. Since each **proton**
or neutron has a relative **mass** of (approximately) **1** and the electrons weigh virtually
nothing, the **number of nucleons** is the same as the **atom's relative mass**.

The nuclide notation of an element summarises information about its atomic structure:

The nucleon number — there are a total of 12
protons and neutrons in a carbon-12 atom.

The proton number — there are
six protons in a carbon atom.

The symbol for the element carbon.

$$^{12}_{6}\text{C}$$

Atomic Structure

Isotopes have the Same Proton Number, but Different Nucleon Numbers

Atoms with the **same number of protons** but **different numbers of neutrons** are called **isotopes**.

Example: Hydrogen has three natural isotopes — hydrogen, deuterium and tritium.
Hydrogen has 1 proton and 0 neutrons.
Deuterium has 1 proton and 1 neutron.
Tritium has 1 proton and 2 neutrons.

Changing the number of **neutrons doesn't affect** the atom's **chemical** properties.

The **number of neutrons** affects the **stability** of the nucleus though.

Unstable nuclei may be **radioactive** and **decay** over time into different nuclei that are more stable (see p.5).

Radioactive Isotopes Can be Used to Find Out How Old Stuff Is

1) All living things contain the same percentage of radioactive **carbon-14** taken in from the atmosphere.

2) After they die, the amount of carbon-14 inside them **decreases** over time as it **decays** to stable elements.

3) Scientists can calculate the **approximate age** of archaeological finds made from dead **organic matter** (e.g. wood, bone) by using the **isotopic data** (amount of each isotope present) to find the percentage of **radioactive carbon-14** that's **left in** the object.

The Specific Charge of a Particle is Equal to its Charge Over its Mass

The **specific charge** of a particle is the ratio of its charge to its mass, given in coulombs per kilogram ($C\,kg^{-1}$). To calculate specific charge, you just divide the charge in C by the mass in kg.

$$\text{Specific charge} = \frac{\text{charge}}{\text{mass}}$$

You could be asked to find the specific charge of any particle, from a **fundamental particle** like an electron, to the nucleus of an atom or an ion.

A fundamental particle is one that you can't break up into anything smaller.

Example: Calculate the specific charge of a proton.

A proton has a **charge** of $+1.60 \times 10^{-19}$ C and a **mass** of 1.67×10^{-27} kg (see p.2).

So specific charge = $(+1.60 \times 10^{-19}) \div (1.67 \times 10^{-27}) = 9.580... \times 10^7 = \mathbf{9.58 \times 10^7\ C\,kg^{-1}}$ **(to 3 s.f.)**

In calculations, always give your answer to the smallest number of significant figures used in the question.

Warm-Up Questions

Q1 List the particles that make up the atom and give their relative charges and relative masses.

Q2 Define the proton number and nucleon number.

Q3 Explain how the amount of carbon-14 in dead organic matter can tell scientists how old it is.

Q4 How could you calculate the specific charge of a particle?

Exam Questions

Q1 Describe the nuclear model of the atom. [2 marks]

Q2 Write down the numbers of protons, neutrons and electrons in a neutral atom of oxygen, $^{16}_{8}O$. [2 marks]

Q3 a) State what is meant by an 'isotope'. [1 mark]

   b) State the similarities and differences between the properties of two isotopes of the same element. [2 marks]

Q4 An alpha particle is the nucleus of a $^4_2$He atom. Calculate the specific charge of an alpha particle. [4 marks]

"Proton no. = no. of protons" — hardly nuclear physics is it... oh wait...

Physics is the science of all things great and small — on these pages you saw the small (like, really really small). That's why it's useful to know about things like relative charge and relative mass — 'one point six seven times ten to the power of negative twenty-seven' is a bit more of a mouthful than 'one'. It all makes perfect sense.

Stable and Unstable Nuclei

Keeping the nucleus stable requires a lot of effort — a bit like Physics then...

The **Strong Nuclear Force** Binds Nucleons Together

There are several different **forces** acting on the nucleons in a nucleus. The two you already know about are **electrostatic** forces from the protons' electric charges, and **gravitational** forces due to the masses of the particles.

If you do the calculations (don't worry, *you* don't have to) you find the repulsion from the **electrostatic force** is much, much **bigger** than the **gravitational** attraction. If these were the only forces acting in the nucleus, the nucleons would **fly apart**. So there must be **another attractive force** that **holds the nucleus together** — called the **strong nuclear force**. (The gravitational force is so small, you can just ignore it.)

The **strong nuclear force** is quite **complicated**:

1) To **hold the nucleus together**, it must be an **attractive force** that's **stronger** than the electrostatic force.
2) Experiments have shown that the strong nuclear force has a **very short range**. It can only hold nucleons together when they're separated by up to **a few femtometres** (1 fm = 1 × 10⁻¹⁵ m) — the size of a nucleus.
3) The **strength** of the strong nuclear force **quickly falls** beyond this distance (see the graph below).
4) Experiments also show that the strong nuclear force **works equally between all nucleons**. This means that the size of the force is the same whether it's proton-proton, neutron-neutron or proton-neutron.
5) At **very small separations**, the strong nuclear force must be **repulsive** or it would **crush** the nucleus to a **point**.

The **Size** of the Strong Nuclear Force **Varies** with **Nucleon Separation**

The **strong nuclear force** can be plotted on a **graph** to show how it changes with the **distance of separation** between **nucleons**. If the **electrostatic force** is also plotted, you can see the **relationship** between these **two forces**.

3) The **electrostatic repulsive** force extends over a much **larger range** (indefinitely, actually).

1) The strong nuclear force is **repulsive** for **very small** separations of nucleons.

You might hear the strong nuclear force called the strong interaction.

2) As nucleon separation **increases past about 0.5 fm**, the **strong nuclear force** becomes **attractive**. It reaches a maximum attractive value and then **falls rapidly** towards zero after about **3 fm**.

α **Emission** Happens in **Very Big Nuclei**

1) **Alpha emission** only happens in **very big** nuclei, like **uranium** and **radium**.
2) The **nuclei** of these atoms are just **too massive** for the strong nuclear force to keep them stable.
3) When an alpha particle is **emitted**:

The **proton number decreases** by two, and the **nucleon number decreases** by **four**.

Alpha particles have a very **short range** — only a few cm in air. This can be seen by observing the tracks left by alpha particles in a **cloud chamber**. You could also use a **Geiger counter** (a device that measures the amount of ionising radiation). Bring it up close to the alpha source, then **move it away** slowly and observe how the **count rate drops**.

The thin line is a cosmic ray particle

Stable and Unstable Nuclei

β⁻ Emission Happens in Neutron-Rich Nuclei

1) **Beta-minus** (usually just called beta) decay is the emission of an **electron** from the **nucleus** along with an **antineutrino**.

2) Beta decay happens in isotopes that are unstable due to being **'neutron rich'** (i.e. they have too many more **neutrons** than **protons** in their nucleus).

3) When a nucleus ejects a beta particle, one of the **neutrons** in the nucleus is **changed** into a **proton**.

> The **proton number increases** by **one**, and the **nucleon number stays the same**.

Beta particles have a much greater range than alpha particles.

nucleon number stays the same

$$^{187}_{75}\text{Re} \longrightarrow {}^{187}_{76}\text{Os} + {}^{0}_{-1}\beta + \bar{\nu}_e$$

proton number increases by 1

In beta decay, you get a tiny neutral particle called an antineutrino released. This antineutrino carries away some energy and momentum.

Neutrinos Were First Hypothesised Due to Observations of Beta Decay

1) Scientists originally thought that the **only** particle emitted from the nucleus during beta decay was an **electron**.

2) However, observations showed that the **energy** of the particles **after** the beta decay was **less** than it was **before**, which didn't fit with the principle of **conservation of energy** (p. 68).

3) In 1930 Wolfgang Pauli suggested **another particle** was being emitted too, and it carried away the **missing energy**. This particle had to be **neutral** (or charge wouldn't be **conserved** in beta decay) and had to have **zero** or **almost zero** mass (as it had never been **detected**).

4) Other discoveries led to Pauli's theory becoming accepted and the particle was named the **neutrino**. (We now know this particle was an antineutrino — p. 6).

5) The neutrino was eventually observed 25 years later, providing evidence for Pauli's hypothesis.

Warm-Up Questions

Q1 What causes an electrostatic force inside the nucleus?
Q2 What evidence suggests the existence of a strong nuclear force?
Q3 Is the strong interaction attractive or repulsive at a nucleon separation of 2 fm?
Q4 Describe the changes that happen in the nucleus during alpha and beta-minus decay.
Q5 What observations led to the hypothesis of the existence of the neutrino?

PRACTICE QUESTIONS

Exam Questions

Q1 The strong nuclear force binds the nucleus together.

   a) Explain why the force must be repulsive at very short distances.
             [1 mark]

   b) Explain why a nucleus containing two protons in unstable, but one containing two protons and two neutrons is stable.
             [2 marks]

Q2 Radium-226 and potassium-40 are both unstable isotopes.

   a) Radium-226 undergoes alpha decay to radon. Complete the balanced nuclear equation for this reaction:

$$^{226}_{88}\text{Ra} \longrightarrow \quad \text{Rn} +$$

             [3 marks]

   b) Potassium-40 (Z = 19, A = 40) undergoes beta decay to calcium. Write a balanced nuclear equation for this reaction.
             [4 marks]

The strong interaction's like nuclear glue...

Energy, momentum, charge and nucleon number (and several other things that you'll find out about in this section) are conserved in every nuclear reaction. That's why the antineutrino in beta decay has to be there.

Particles and Antiparticles

"I cannae do it Cap'n — their electron-antineutrino ray gun's interfering with my antineutron positron reading..."

Photons are Packets of Electromagnetic Radiation

Visible light is just one type of electromagnetic radiation. The **electromagnetic spectrum** is a continuous spectrum of **all** the possible frequencies of electromagnetic radiation.

Increasing frequency ← → Increasing wavelength

RADIO WAVES | MICRO-WAVES | INFRA-RED | VISIBLE LIGHT | ULTRA-VIOLET | X-RAYS | GAMMA RAYS

The **frequency** f and **wavelength** λ are linked by $f = \frac{c}{\lambda}$, where $c = 3.00 \times 10^8$ ms^{-1} is the **speed of light** in a vacuum (sometimes called the speed of light **in vacuo**).

Electromagnetic radiation exists as **photons** of energy (page 16). The **energy** of a photon depends on the frequency of the radiation:

$$E = hf = \frac{hc}{\lambda}$$

h is the Planck constant, equal to 6.63×10^{-34} Js.

Every Particle has an Antiparticle

1) Each particle has a **matching antiparticle** with the **same mass** and **rest energy** (more later), but with **opposite charge** (amongst other things).

2) For instance, an **antiproton** is a **negatively-charged** particle with the same mass as the **proton**, and the **antineutrino** is the antiparticle of the **neutrino** — it doesn't do much either.

Particle/Antiparticle	Symbol	Relative Charge	Mass (kg)	Rest Energy (MeV)
proton	p	+1	$1.67(3) \times 10^{-27}$	938(.3)
antiproton	$\bar{p}$	−1		
neutron	n	0	$1.67(5) \times 10^{-27}$	939(.6)
antineutron	$\bar{n}$			
electron	e^-	−1	9.11×10^{-31}	0.51(1)
positron	e^+	+1		
neutrino	ν_e	0	0	0
antineutrino	$\bar{\nu}_e$			

These are actually an electron-neutrino and an electron-antineutrino (p. 12).

Luckily, in the exam you'll be given all the **masses** in kg and **rest energies** in MeV of each of these particles and their antiparticles. You just need to remember that the **mass** and **rest energy** are the **same** for a particle and its antiparticle. Neutrinos and antineutrinos are incredibly tiny — you can assume they have zero mass and zero rest energy.

1 MeV = 1 × 10⁶ eV. There's more on eV (electron volts) on p. 18.

You can Create Matter and Antimatter from Energy

You've probably heard about the **equivalence** of energy and mass. It all comes out of Einstein's Special Theory of Relativity. **Energy** can turn into **mass** and **mass** can turn into **energy** if you know how. The **rest energy** of a particle is just the 'energy equivalent' of the particle's **mass**, measured in MeV. You can work it all out using the formula $E = mc^2$, but you won't be expected to do the calculations for AS.

When **energy** is converted into **mass** you get **equal amounts** of **matter** and **antimatter**.

Fire **two protons** at each other at high speed and you'll end up with a lot of **energy** at the point of impact. This energy might be converted into **more particles**.

If an extra **proton** is formed then there will always be an **antiproton** to go with it. It's called **pair production**.

Particles and Antiparticles

Each **Particle-Antiparticle Pair** is Produced from a **Single Photon**

Energy that gets **converted** into **matter** and **antimatter** is in the form of a **photon** (p.16). Pair production only happens if **one photon** has enough energy to produce that much mass — only **gamma ray** photons have enough energy. It also tends to happen near a **nucleus**, which helps conserve momentum.

You usually get **electron-positron** pairs produced (rather than any other pair) — because they have a relatively **low mass**.

The particle tracks are curved because there's usually a magnetic field present in particle physics experiments. They curve in opposite directions because of the opposite charges on the electron and positron.

The **minimum energy** for a photon to undergo **pair production** is the **total rest energy** of the particles produced. The particle and antiparticle each have a rest energy of E_0, so:

$$E_{min} = hf_{min} = 2E_0$$

The **Opposite** of **Pair-Production** is **Annihilation**

When a **particle** meets its **antiparticle** the result is **annihilation**. All the **mass** of the particle and antiparticle gets converted back to **energy**. Antiparticles can usually only exist for a fraction of a second before this happens, so you don't get them in ordinary matter.

OR

The electron and positron annihilate and their mass is converted into the energy of a pair of gamma ray photons to conserve momentum.

An annihilation is between a particle-antiparticle pair, which both have a rest energy E_0. **Both** photons need to have a **minimum energy**, E_{min}, which when added together equals at least $2E_0$ for **energy** to be **conserved** in this interaction. So $2E_{min} = 2E_0$ and:

$$E_{min} = hf_{min} = E_0$$

Example: Calculate the maximum wavelength of one of the photons produced when an electron and positron annihilate each other.

For annihilation, minimum photon energy $E_{min} = hf_{min} = E_0$. Remember $f = \frac{c}{\lambda}$, so $\frac{hc}{\lambda_{max}} = E_0$.

So $\lambda_{max} = \frac{hc}{E_0} = \frac{(6.63 \times 10^{-34}) \times (3.00 \times 10^8)}{(0.511 \times 10^6) \times (1.60 \times 10^{-19})} = 2.432... \times 10^{-12} = \textbf{2.43} \times \textbf{10}^{-12}$ **m** (to 3 s.f.)

The Planck constant is in J, so you need to convert E_0 from MeV to J.

Warm-Up Questions

Q1 Describe the properties of an electron-antineutrino.
Q2 Give one similarity and one difference between a proton and an antiproton.
Q3 What is pair production?
Q4 What happens when a proton collides with an antiproton?

Exam Questions

Q1 Write down an equation for the reaction between a positron and an electron and state the name for this type of reaction. [2 marks]

Q2 Explain what causes extra particles to be created when two particles collide. [2 marks]

Q3 Give a reason why the reaction: $p + p \rightarrow p + p + n$ is not possible. [1 mark]

Q4 A photon produces an electron-positron pair, each with 9.84×10^{-14} J of energy. Calculate the frequency of the photon. [2 marks]

This really is Physics at its ~~hardest~~ grooviest...

Inertial dampers are off-line Captain.........oops, no — it's just these false ears making me feel dizzy. Anyway — you'd need to carry an awful lot of antimatter to provide enough energy to run a spaceship. Plus, it's not the easiest to store...

Forces and Exchange Particles

*Having learnt about all those lovely particles and antiparticles, you now have the esteemed privilege of learning about yet another weirdy thing called a **gauge boson**. To the casual observer this might not seem **entirely fair**. And I have to say, I'd be with them.*

Forces are Caused by Particle Exchange

You can't have **instantaneous action at a distance** (according to Einstein, anyway). So, when two particles **interact**, something must **happen** to let one particle know that the other one's there. That's the idea behind **exchange particles**.

1) **Repulsion** — Each time the **ball** is thrown or caught the people get **pushed apart**. It happens because the ball carries **momentum**.

   Particle exchange also explains **attraction**, but you need a bit more imagination.

2) **Attraction** — Each time the **boomerang** is **thrown or caught** the people **get pushed together**. (In real life, you'd probably fall in first.)

←—REPULSION—→

→ATTRACTION←

These exchange particles are called **gauge bosons**.

The **repulsion** between two **protons** is caused by the **exchange** of **virtual photons**, which are the gauge bosons of the **electromagnetic** force. Gauge bosons are **virtual** particles — they only exist for a **very short time**.

There are Four Fundamental Forces

All forces in nature are caused by four **fundamental** forces — the strong nuclear force, the weak nuclear force, the electromagnetic force and gravity. Each one has its **own gauge boson** and these are the ones you have to learn:

Type of Interaction	Gauge Boson	Particles Affected
electromagnetic	virtual photon (symbol, γ)	charged particles only
weak	W^+, W^-	all types
strong	pions (π^+, π^-, π^0)	hadrons only

Particle physicists never bother about gravity because it's so incredibly feeble compared with the other types of interaction. Gravity only really matters when you've got big masses like stars and planets.

In the strong nuclear force, pions are described as being exchanged between nucleons. You might also see it described as gluons being exchanged between quarks (p. 13).

The **Larger** the **Mass** of the **Gauge Boson**, the **Shorter** the **Range** of the **Force**

1) The **W bosons** have a **mass** of about **100 times that of a proton**, which gives the weak force a **very short range**. Creating a **virtual W particle** uses **so much energy** that it can only exist for a **very short time** and it **can't travel far**.

2) On the other hand, the **photon** has **zero mass**, which gives you a force with **infinite range**.

You can use **Diagrams** to Show What's **Going In** and What's **Coming Out**

Particle interactions can be hard to get your head around. A **neat way** of **solving problems** is by **drawing simple diagrams** of particle interactions rather than doing **calculations**.

1) **Gauge bosons** are represented by **wiggly lines** (technical term).

2) Other **particles** are represented by **straight lines**.

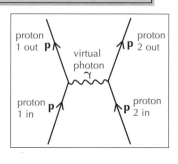

proton 1 out **p**   virtual photon γ **p** proton 2 out

proton 1 in **p**   **p** proton 2 in

Forces and Exchange Particles

*You can draw simple diagrams of **loads** of interactions, but you **only** need to learn these ones for your exams.*

You Need to Be Able to **Draw Diagrams** of these **Interactions**

Electromagnetic Repulsion

This is the easiest of the lot. When two particles with **equal charges** get close to each other, they **repel**.

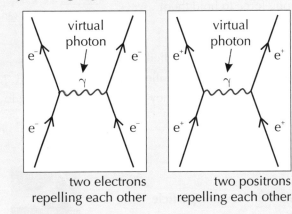

two electrons repelling each other

two positrons repelling each other

RULES FOR DRAWING PARTICLE INTERACTION DIAGRAMS:

1) **Incoming** particles start at the bottom of the diagram and move upwards.

2) The **baryons** (p.10) and **leptons** (p.12) can't cross from one side to the other.

3) Make sure the charges on both sides balance. The **W** bosons carry **charge** from one side of the diagram to the other.

4) A **W⁻** particle going to the **left** has the same effect as a **W⁺** particle going to the **right**.

Electron Capture and Electron-proton Collisions

Electrons and protons are of course attracted by the **electromagnetic interaction** between them, but if a proton **captures** an electron, the **weak interaction** can make this interaction happen.

$$p + e^- \rightarrow n + \nu_e$$

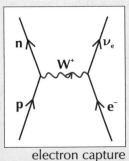

electron capture

You also need to know about **electron-proton collisions**, where an electron **collides** with a proton. The equation is just the same as electron capture but in the diagram a **W⁻ boson** goes from the **electron** to the **proton** instead of a W⁺ travelling the other way.

Beta-plus and Beta-minus Decay

β⁻ decay

β⁺ decay

$$n \rightarrow p + e^- + \bar{\nu}_e$$

$$p \rightarrow n + e^+ + \nu_e$$

You get an **antineutrino** in β⁻ decay and a **neutrino** in β⁺ decay so that **lepton number** (p.12) is conserved.

You'll see on p.14 that when a proton changes to a neutron or vice versa, it has to be the weak interaction.

Warm-Up Questions

Q1 List the four fundamental forces in nature.

Q2 Explain what a virtual particle is.

Q3 Draw a simple diagram to show the particles involved in a beta-minus decay interaction.

Q4 Which gauge bosons are exchanged in weak interactions?

Exam Questions

Q1 Describe how the force of electromagnetic repulsion between two protons is explained by particle exchange. [2 marks]

Q2 Draw a diagram to show the particle interaction when an electron and a proton collide. Label all the particles involved and state clearly which type of interaction is involved. [3 marks]

I need a drink...

Urrrgghhhh... eyes... glazed... brain... melting... ears... bleeding... help me... help me...

help me...

Classification of Particles

*There are loads of different types of particle apart from the ones you get in normal matter (protons, neutrons, etc.).
They only appear in cosmic rays and in particle accelerators, and they often decay very quickly so they're
difficult to get a handle on. Nonetheless, you need to learn about a load of them and their properties.
Stick with it — you'll get there.*

Hadrons are Particles that Feel the Strong Nuclear Force (e.g. Protons and Neutrons)

1) The **nucleus** of an atom is made up of **protons** and **neutrons** (déjà vu).

2) Since the **protons** are **positively charged** they need a strong force to hold them
   together. This is called the **strong nuclear force** or the **strong interaction**
   (who said physicists lack imagination...). See page 4 for details.

   (Leptons are an example
   of particles that can't.
   See page 12.)

3) **Not all particles** can **feel** the **strong nuclear force** — the ones that **can** are called **hadrons**.

4) Hadrons aren't **fundamental** particles. They're made up of **smaller particles** called **quarks** (see pages 13–15).

5) There are **two** types of **hadrons** — **baryons** (and anti-baryons) and **mesons**. They're classified according to the
   number of **quarks** that make them up, but don't worry about that for now.

Protons and Neutrons are Baryons

1) It's helpful to think of **protons** and **neutrons** as **two versions** of the **same particle**
   — the **nucleon**. They just have **different electric charges**.

2) **Protons** and **neutrons** are both **baryons**.

3) There are **other baryons** that you don't get in normal matter — like **sigmas** (Σ)
   — they're **short-lived** and you **don't** need to **know about them** (woohoo!).

Baryon and Meson felt
the strong interaction.

The Proton is the Only Stable Baryon

All **baryons** — except the proton — are **unstable**. This means that they **decay** to become other **particles**.
The **particles** a baryon ends up as depends on what it started as, but it **always** includes a **proton**.
Protons are the only **stable baryons** — they don't decay (as far as we know).

All baryons except protons decay to a **proton**.

Some theories predict that protons should
decay with a very long half-life, but there's
no evidence for it at the moment.

Antiprotons and Antineutrons are Antibaryons

The **antiparticles** of protons and neutrons — **antiprotons** and **antineutrons** — are **antibaryons**.
But, if you remember from page 7, **antiparticles** are **annihilated** when they meet the
corresponding **particle** — which means that you **don't** find **antibaryons** in ordinary matter.

The Number of Baryons in an Interaction is called the Baryon Number

The **baryon number** is the number of baryons. (A bit like **nucleon number** but including unusual baryons like Σ too.)
The **proton** and the **neutron** each have a baryon number $B = +1$. **Antibaryons** have a baryon number $B = -1$.
Other particles (i.e. things that aren't baryons) are given a baryon number $B = 0$.

Baryon number is a **quantum number** that must be **conserved** in any interaction — that means it can only take on
a **certain set of values** (so you can't have 2.7981 baryons, or 1.991112 baryons... you get the idea).

When an **interaction** happens, the **baryon number** on either side of the interaction has to be the **same**.
You can use this fact to **predict** whether an **interaction** will **happen** — if the numbers don't match, it can't happen.

The **total baryon number** in **any** particle interaction **never changes**.

Classification of Particles

Neutrons are Baryons that Decay into Protons

You saw on pages 5 and 9 that **beta decay** involves a **neutron** changing into a **proton**. This happens when there are many **more neutrons** than **protons** in a nucleus or when a **neutron** is **by itself**, **outside** of a nucleus. Beta decay is caused by the **weak interaction** (see page 14).

When a neutron decays, it forms a **proton**, an **electron** and an **antineutrino**:

$$n \rightarrow p + e^- + \bar{\nu}_e$$

Electrons and **antineutrinos** aren't baryons (they're **leptons**, as you'll see on the next page), so they have a baryon number **B = 0**. **Neutrons** and **protons** are baryons, so have a baryon number **B = 1**. This means that the **baryon numbers** on both sides are **equal** (to 1), so the interaction **can** happen.

The Mesons You Need to Know About are Pions and Kaons

The second type of hadron you need to know about is the **meson**.
1) **All mesons** are **unstable** and have **baryon number B = 0** (because they're not baryons).
2) **Pions** (π-mesons) are the **lightest mesons**. You get **three versions** with different **electric charges** — π^+, π^0 and π^-. You get **loads** of pions in **high-energy particle collisions** like those studied at the **CERN** particle accelerator.
3) **Kaons** (K-mesons) are **heavier** and more **unstable** than **pions**. You get different ones like K^+ and K^0. Kaons have a very **short lifetime** and **decay** into **pions**.
4) Pions and kaons were **discovered** in **cosmic rays** — cosmic ray showers are a source of both particles. You can observe the tracks of these particles with a **cloud chamber** (see p.4).
5) Mesons **interact** with **baryons** via the **strong force**.

Pion interactions swap protons with neutrons and neutrons with protons, but leave the overall baryon number unchanged.

Summary of Hadron Properties

DON'T PANIC if you don't understand all this yet. For now, just **learn** these properties.
You'll need to work through to the end of page 15 to see how it **all fits together**.

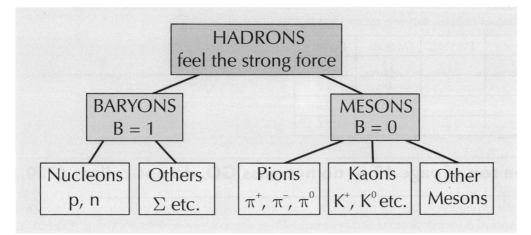

Classification of Particles

Leptons (e.g. Electrons and Neutrinos) Don't Feel the Strong Nuclear Force

1) **Leptons** are **fundamental particles** and they **don't** feel the **strong nuclear force**.
They only really **interact** with other particles via the **weak interaction** (along with
a bit of gravitational force and the electromagnetic force as well if they're charged).

2) **Electrons (e⁻)** are **stable** and very **familiar**, but — you guessed it — there are also **other leptons**,
such as the **muon (μ^-)**, that are just like **heavy electrons**.

3) **Muons** are **unstable**, and **decay** eventually into **ordinary electrons**.

4) The **electron** and **muon** leptons each come with their **own neutrino**, ν_e and ν_μ.

5) **Neutrinos** have **zero** or **almost zero** mass, and **zero electric charge** — so they don't do much.
Neutrinos only take part in **weak interactions** (see p.14). In fact, a neutrino can
pass right through the Earth without **anything** happening to it.

You Have to Count the Types of Lepton Separately

Like the baryon number, the **lepton number** is
just the number of **leptons**. **Each lepton** is given a
lepton number of **+1**, but the **electron** and **muon**
types of lepton have to be **counted separately**.
You get **different** lepton numbers, L_e and L_μ.

All the leptons and lepton-neutrinos have their
own **antiparticle** too — no surprises there. They
have the **opposite charge** and **lepton numbers**
to their matching particles. For example, the
antimuon μ^+ has charge = +1, $L_e = 0$ and $L_\mu = -1$.

Name	Symbol	Charge	L_e	L_μ
electron	e^-	-1	$+1$	0
electron-neutrino	ν_e	0	$+1$	0
muon	μ^-	-1	0	$+1$
muon-neutrino	ν_μ	0	0	$+1$

Warm-Up Questions

Q1 List the differences between a hadron and a lepton.

Q2 Which is the only stable baryon (probably)?

Q3 A particle collision at CERN produces 2 protons, 3 pions and 1 neutron.
What is the total baryon number of these particles?

Q4 Which two particles have lepton number $L_\mu = +1$?

PRACTICE QUESTIONS

Exam Questions

Q1 List all the decay products of the neutron.
Explain why this decay cannot be due to the strong interaction. [3 marks]

Q2 Initially, the muon was incorrectly identified as a meson.
Explain why the muon is not a meson. [3 marks]

Q3 A sodium atom contains 11 electrons, 11 protons and 12 neutrons. Which row in the table contains
the correct numbers of hadrons, baryons, mesons and leptons in a sodium atom? [1 mark]

	Hadrons	Baryons	Mesons	Leptons
A	12	11	12	11
B	23	23	0	11
C	23	0	23	23
D	12	11	0	23

Go back to the top of page 10 — do not pass GO, do not collect £200...

Do it. Go back and read it again. I promise — read these pages a few times and you'll start to see a pattern. There are hadrons that feel the strong force, leptons that don't. Hadrons are either baryons or mesons, and they're all weird except for those well-known baryons: protons and neutrons. There are loads of leptons, including good old electrons.

Quarks

Quarks may sound like a bizarre concept, but they weren't just made up willy-nilly. Large teams of scientists and engineers all over the world worked for years to come up with the info on these pages.

Quarks are Fundamental Particles

Quarks are the **building blocks** for **hadrons** (baryons and mesons). Antiparticles of hadrons are made from **antiquarks**.

1) To make **protons** and **neutrons** you only need two types of quark — the **up** quark (**u**) and the **down** quark (**d**).
2) An extra one called the **strange** quark (**s**) lets you make more particles with a property called **strangeness**.

Strangeness is Only Conserved Some of the Time

1) **Strangeness**, like baryon number, is a **quantum number** (see p.10) — it can only take a certain set of values.
2) Strange particles, such as kaons, are **created** via the **strong** interaction but **decay** via the **weak** interaction.
3) Here's the catch — strangeness is **conserved** in the **strong interaction**, but **not** in the **weak interaction** (p.14).
4) That means strange particles are **always produced in pairs** (e.g. K^+ and K^-).
   One has a strangeness of +1, and the other has a strangeness of –1, so the overall strangeness of 0 is **conserved**.

Quarks and Antiquarks have Opposite Properties

The **antiquarks** have **opposite properties** to the quarks — as you'd expect.

QUARKS	Name	Symbol	Charge	Baryon number	Strangeness
	up	u	$+\,^2/_3$	$+\,^1/_3$	0
	down	d	$-\,^1/_3$	$+\,^1/_3$	0
	strange	s	$-\,^1/_3$	$+\,^1/_3$	–1

ANTIQUARKS	Name	Symbol	Charge	Baryon number	Strangeness
	anti-up	$\bar{u}$	$-\,^2/_3$	$-\,^1/_3$	0
	anti-down	$\bar{d}$	$+\,^1/_3$	$-\,^1/_3$	0
	anti-strange	$\bar{s}$	$+\,^1/_3$	$-\,^1/_3$	+1

Baryons are Made from Three Quarks

Evidence for quarks came from **hitting protons** with **high-energy electrons**.
The way the **electrons scattered** showed that there were **three concentrations of charge** (quarks) **inside** the proton.

Proton = **uud**

Total charge
$= ^2/_3 + ^2/_3 - ^1/_3 = 1$
Baryon number
$= ^1/_3 + ^1/_3 + ^1/_3 = 1$

Antiproton = $\bar{u}\bar{u}\bar{d}$

Total charge
$= -^2/_3 - ^2/_3 + ^1/_3 = -1$
Baryon number
$= -^1/_3 - ^1/_3 - ^1/_3 = -1$

Neutron = **udd**

Total charge
$= ^2/_3 - ^1/_3 - ^1/_3 = 0$
Baryon number
$= ^1/_3 + ^1/_3 + ^1/_3 = 1$

Antineutron = $\bar{u}\bar{d}\bar{d}$

Total charge
$= -^2/_3 + ^1/_3 + ^1/_3 = 0$
Baryon number
$= -^1/_3 - ^1/_3 - ^1/_3 = -1$

Quarks

Mesons are a Quark and an Antiquark

Pions are just made from combinations of **up**, **down**, **anti-up** and **anti-down** quarks.
Kaons have **strangeness** so you need to put in **s** quarks as well (remember, the **s** quark has a strangeness of S = –1).

Before we move on, it's worth mentioning that the π^- meson is just the **antiparticle** of the π^+ meson, the **K**$^-$ meson is the antiparticle of the **K**$^+$ meson, and the **antiparticle** of a π^0 meson is **itself**. It all makes sense when you look at the quark compositions to the right...

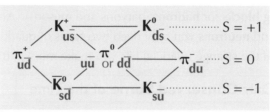

$$K^+_{us} \quad\quad K^0_{ds} \quad\cdots\cdots\quad S = +1$$
$$\pi^+_{ud} \quad \frac{\pi^0}{u\overline{u} \text{ or } d\overline{d}} \quad \pi^-_{du} \quad\cdots\quad S = 0$$
$$\overline{K^0}_{sd} \quad\quad K^-_{su} \quad\cdots\cdots\quad S = -1$$

Physicists love patterns. Gaps in patterns like this predicted the existence of particles that were actually found later in experiments. Great stuff.

The Weak Interaction is something that Changes the Quark Type

In β^- decay a **neutron** is changed into a **proton** — in other words **udd** changes into **uud**. It means turning a **d** quark into a **u** quark. Only the weak interaction can do this.

neutron   proton

Some unstable isotopes like **carbon-11** decay by β^+ emission. In this case a **proton** changes to a **neutron**, so a **u** quark changes to a **d** quark and we get:

proton   neutron

Four Properties are Conserved in Particle Interactions

Charge is Always Conserved

In **any** particle interaction, the **total charge** after the interaction must equal the total charge before the interaction.

Energy and momentum are also always conserved in particle interactions.

Baryon Number is Always Conserved

Just like with charge, in **any** particle interaction, the **baryon number** after the interaction must equal the baryon number before the interaction.

Dylan was committed to conserving strangeness.

Strangeness is Conserved in Strong Interactions

The **only** way to change the **type** of quark is with the **weak interaction**, so in strong interactions there has to be the same number of strange quarks at the beginning as at the end. In weak interactions, strangeness can change by –1, 0 or +1. The interaction $K^- + p \rightarrow n + \pi^0$ is fine for **charge** and **baryon number** but not for **strangeness** — so it won't happen. The negative kaon has an **s** quark in it.

Conservation of Lepton Number is a Bit More Complicated

The **different types** of lepton number have to be conserved **separately**.

1) For example, the interaction
   $\pi^- \rightarrow \mu^- + \overline{\nu}_\mu$ has $L_\mu = 0$ at the start and $L_\mu = 1 - 1 = 0$ at the end, so it's OK.
   Similarly, $n \rightarrow p + e^- + \overline{\nu}_e$ is fine. $L_e = 0$ at the start and $L_e = 1 - 1 = 0$ at the end.
2) On the other hand, the interaction $\nu_\mu + \mu^- \rightarrow e^- + \nu_e$ can't happen.
   At the start $L_\mu = 2$ and $L_e = 0$, but at the end $L_\mu = 0$ and $L_e = 2$.

Lepton number is a quantum number, just like baryon number and strangeness.

Quarks

There's **No Such Thing** as a **Free Quark**

What if you **blasted** a **proton** with **enough energy** — could you **separate out** the quarks? Nope. Your energy just gets changed into more **quarks and antiquarks** — it's **pair production** again and you just make **mesons**. It's not possible to get a quark by itself — this is called **quark confinement**.

We're Still **Searching** for Particles

As time goes on, our knowledge and understanding of particle physics **changes**.

Simon was practising
quack confinement.

1) **New theories** are created to try to explain observations from experiments.
   Sometimes, physicists hypothesise a new **particle** and the **properties** they expect it to have.
   E.g. the **neutrino** was hypothesised due to observations of beta decay.

2) **Experiments** to try to find the existence of this new particle are then carried out. Results from different experiments are **combined** to try to **confirm** the new particle. If it exists, the theory is **more likely** to be correct and the scientific community start to accept it — it's **validated**.

3) It's not quite that simple though. Experiments in particle physics often need particles travelling at incredibly **high speeds** (close to the speed of light). This can only be achieved using **particle accelerators**. These huge pieces of equipment are very **expensive** to build and run. This means that **large groups** of scientists and engineers from all over the **world** have to **collaborate** to be able to fund these experiments.

Example: Paul Dirac predicted the existence of **antimatter** in 1928. His theory was **validated** with the observation of the **positron** and, over the years, more and more observations of antiparticles. Nowadays, it's **accepted** that antimatter exists, but there are still **questions**. For example, there should have been **equal amounts** of matter and antimatter created when the universe was formed, but **almost everything** we observe is made of **matter**.

Scientists are trying to figure out what happened to all the antimatter by studying the differences in behaviour of matter and antimatter particles using the **Large Hadron Collider (LHC)** at **CERN**. The LHC is a **17 mile long** particle accelerator costing around **£3 billion** to build and **£15 million** per year to run. Some **10,000** scientists from **100** countries are involved.

ATLAS, just one of many experiments the LHC at CERN is used for, involves around 3000 scientists from 38 different countries.

Warm-Up Questions

Q1 What is a quark?

Q2 Kaons are produced by the strong interaction. Why must they be produced in pairs?

Q3 By how much can the strangeness change in a weak interaction?

Q4 Which type of particle is made from a quark and an antiquark?

Q5 Describe how a neutron is made up from quarks.

Q6 List six quantities that are conserved in strong particle interactions.

Exam Questions

Q1 a) Write down the quark composition of the π^-. [1 mark]

   b) Explain how the charges of the quarks give rise to its charge. [1 mark]

Q2 Explain how the quark composition is changed in the β^- decay of the neutron. [2 marks]

Q3 Give two reasons why the reaction $p + p \rightarrow p + K^+$ does not happen. [2 marks]

A physical property called strangeness — how cool is that...

True, there's a lot of information here, but this page really does tie up a lot of the stuff on the last few pages. Learn as much as you can from this three-page spread, then go back to page 13, and work back through to here. Don't expect to understand it all — but you'll definitely find it much easier to learn when you can see how all the bits fit together.

The Photoelectric Effect

I think they should rename 'the photoelectric effect' as 'the piece-of-cake effect' — it's not easy, I just like cake.

Shining Light on a Metal can Release Electrons

If you shine **light** of a **high enough frequency** onto the **surface of a metal**, the metal will **emit electrons**. For **most** metals, this **frequency** falls in the **UV** range.

'Light' means any EM radiation — not just visible light.

1) **Free electrons** on the **surface** of the metal **absorb energy** from the light.

2) If an electron **absorbs enough** energy, the **bonds** holding it to the metal **break** and the electron is **released**.

3) This is called the **photoelectric effect** and the electrons emitted are called **photoelectrons**.

ultraviolet radiation

electrons

You don't need to know the details of any experiments on this, you just need to learn the three main conclusions:

Conclusion 1   For a given metal, no photoelectrons are emitted if the radiation has a frequency below a certain value — called the threshold frequency.

These are the two that had scientists puzzled. They can't be explained using wave theory.

Conclusion 2   The photoelectrons are emitted with a variety of kinetic energies ranging from zero to some maximum value. This value of maximum kinetic energy increases with the frequency of the radiation, and is unaffected by the intensity of the radiation.

Conclusion 3   The number of photoelectrons emitted per second is proportional to the intensity of the radiation.

Intensity is the power (the energy transferred per second) hitting a given area of the metal (see page 33).

The Photoelectric Effect Couldn't be Explained by Wave Theory...

According to wave theory:
1) For a particular frequency of light, the **energy** carried is **proportional** to the **intensity** of the beam.
2) The energy carried by the light would be **spread evenly** over the wavefront.
3) **Each** free electron on the surface of the metal would gain a **bit of energy** from each incoming wave.
4) Gradually, each electron would gain **enough energy** to leave the metal.

SO... The **higher the intensity** of the wave, the **more energy** it should transfer to each electron — the kinetic energy should increase with **intensity**. There's **no explanation** for the **kinetic energy** depending only on the **frequency**.

There is also **no explanation** for the **threshold frequency**. According to **wave theory**, the electrons should be emitted **eventually**, no matter what the **frequency** is.

...But it Could be Explained by Einstein's Photon Model of Light

1) **Einstein** suggested that **EM waves** (and the energy they carry) **exist** in discrete packets — called **photons**.

2) The **energy carried** by one of these **photons** is:

$$E = hf = \frac{hc}{\lambda}$$

where h = Planck's constant = 6.63×10^{-34} Js
and c = speed of light in a vacuum = 3.00×10^{8} ms^{-1}

You might have seen this formula before on page 6.

3) Einstein saw these photons of light as having a **one-on-one**, **particle-like** interaction with **an electron** in a **metal surface**. A photon would **transfer all** its **energy** to **one, specific electron**.

According to the photon model:
1) When light hits its surface, the metal is **bombarded** by photons.
2) If one of these photons **collides** with a free electron, the electron will gain energy equal to hf.

Before an electron can **leave** the surface of the metal, it needs enough energy to **break the bonds holding it there**. This energy is called the **work function** (which has the symbol ϕ (phi)) and its **value** depends on the **metal**.

The Photoelectric Effect

The **Photon Model** Explains the **Threshold Frequency...**

1) If the energy **gained** by an electron (on the surface of the metal) from a photon is **greater** than the **work function**, the electron is **emitted**.

2) If it **isn't**, the metal will heat up, but **no electrons** will be emitted.

3) Since, for **electrons** to be released, $hf \geq \phi$, the **threshold frequency** must be:

$$f = \frac{\phi}{h}$$

...and the **Maximum Kinetic Energy**

1) The **energy transferred** to an electron is **hf**.

2) The **kinetic energy** the electron will be carrying when it **leaves** the metal is **hf minus** any energy it's **lost** on the way out. Electrons **deeper** down in the metal lose more energy than the electrons on the **surface**, which explains the **range** of energies.

3) The **minimum** amount of energy it can lose is the **work function**, so the **maximum kinetic energy** of a photoelectron, $E_{k\,(max)}$, is given by the photoelectric equation:

$$hf = \phi + E_{k\,(max)}$$ where $$E_{k\,(max)} = \frac{1}{2}mv_{max}^2$$

4) The **kinetic energy** of the electrons is **independent of the intensity** (the **number** of photons **per second** on an **area**, p.33), as they can **only absorb one photon** at a time. Increasing the **intensity** just means **more photons per second** on an **area** — each photon has the **same energy** as before.

The **Stopping Potential** Gives the **Maximum Kinetic Energy**

1) The **maximum kinetic energy** can be measured using the idea of **stopping potential**.

2) The **emitted electrons** are made to lose their energy by **doing work** against an applied **potential difference**.

3) The **stopping potential**, V_s, is the p.d. needed to stop the **fastest** moving electrons, with $E_{k\,(max)}$.

4) The **work done** by the p.d. in **stopping** the fastest electrons is equal to the **energy** they were carrying:

work done = p.d. × charge (see p.82)

$$eV_s = E_{k\,(max)}$$

where e = charge on the electron = 1.60×10^{-19} C, V_s = stopping potential in V, and $E_{k\,(max)}$ is measured in J.

Work done = zero.

Warm-Up Questions

Q1 Explain what the photoelectric effect is.
Q2 What three conclusions were drawn from experimentation on the photoelectric effect?
Q3 What is meant by the work function of a metal?
Q4 How is the maximum kinetic energy of a photoelectron related to the work function?
Q5 Explain what is meant by the stopping potential. Write down a formula relating stopping potential and $E_{k\,(max)}$.

PRACTICE QUESTIONS

Exam Questions

Q1 An isolated zinc plate with neutral charge is exposed to high-frequency ultraviolet light. State and explain the effect of the ultraviolet light on the charge of the plate. [2 marks]

Q2 Explain why photoelectric emission from a metal surface only occurs when the frequency of the incident radiation exceeds a certain threshold value. [2 marks]

I'm so glad we got that all cleared up...

The most important bits here are why wave theory doesn't explain the phenomenon of the photoelectric effect, and why the photon theory does. A good way to learn conceptual stuff like this is to try to explain it to someone else.

Energy Levels and Photon Emission

Quantum theory doesn't really make much sense — to anyone. It works though, so it's hard to argue with.

Electrons in Atoms Exist in Discrete Energy Levels

1) **Electrons** in an **atom** can **only exist** in certain **well-defined energy levels**. Each level is given a **number**, with **n = 1** representing the **ground state**.

2) Electrons can **move down** energy levels by **emitting** a **photon**.

3) Since these **transitions** are between **definite energy levels**, the **energy** of **each photon** emitted can **only** take a **certain allowed value**.

4) The diagram on the right shows the **energy levels** for **atomic hydrogen**.

5) The **energies involved** are **so tiny** that it makes sense to use a more **appropriate unit** than the **joule**. The **electronvolt (eV)** is defined as:

> The **kinetic energy carried** by an **electron** after it has been **accelerated** through a **potential difference** of **1 volt**.

energy gained by electron (eV)
= accelerating voltage (V)

$$1\text{ eV} = 1.60 \times 10^{-19}\text{ J}$$

The ground state is the lowest energy state of the atom.

LEVEL   ENERGY

n = ∞   zero energy
n = 5 -8.6×10^{-20} J or -0.54 eV
n = 4 -1.4×10^{-19} J or -0.85 eV

n = 3 -2.4×10^{-19} J or -1.5 eV

n = 2 -5.4×10^{-19} J or -3.4 eV

transitions

n = 1 -2.2×10^{-18} J or -13.6 eV

6) On the diagram, energies are labelled in **both units** for **comparison's** sake.

7) The **energy** carried by each **photon** is **equal** to the **difference in energies** between the **two levels**. The equation below shows a **transition** between a higher energy level n = 2 where the electrons have energy E_2 and a lower energy level n = 1 with electrons of energy E_1:

$$\Delta E = E_2 - E_1 = hf = \frac{hc}{\lambda}$$

The energies are only negative because of how "zero energy" is defined. Just one of those silly convention things — don't worry about it.

8) Electrons can also **move up** energy levels if they **absorb a photon** with the **exact energy difference** between the two levels. The movement of an electron to a higher energy level is called **excitation**.

9) If an electron is **removed** from an atom, we say the atom is **ionised**. The energy of each **energy level** within an atom gives the amount of **energy** needed to **remove an electron** in that level from the atom. The **ionisation energy** of an atom is the amount of energy needed to completely remove an electron from the atom from the **ground state (n = 1)**.

Fluorescent Tubes use Excited Electrons to Produce Light

1) **Fluorescent tubes** contain **mercury vapour**, across which an initial **high voltage** is applied. This **high voltage** accelerates **fast-moving free electrons** that **ionise** some of the **mercury atoms**, producing **more** free electrons.

2) When this flow of free electrons **collides** with electrons in **other mercury atoms**, the electrons in the mercury atoms are **excited** to **higher energy levels**.

3) When these **excited electrons** return to their **ground states**, they emit **photons** in the **UV** range.

4) A **phosphor coating** on the **inside** of the tube **absorbs** these **photons**, exciting its **electrons** to **much higher orbits**. These electrons then **cascade** down the **energy levels**, **emitting** many **lower energy photons** in the form of **visible light**.

Fluorescent Tubes Produce Line Emission Spectra

1) If you **split** the light from a **fluorescent tube** with a **prism** or a **diffraction grating** (see pages 36-37), you get a **line spectrum**.

2) A line spectrum is seen as a **series** of **bright lines** against a **black background**.

3) Each **line** corresponds to a **particular wavelength** of light **emitted** by the source.

4) Since only certain photon energies are allowed, you only see the **wavelengths** corresponding to these energies.

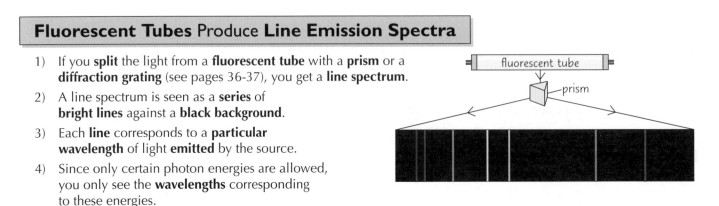

fluorescent tube

prism

Energy Levels and Photon Emission

Shining White Light through a Cool Gas gives an Absorption Spectrum

Continuous Spectra Contain All Possible Wavelengths

1) The **spectrum** of white light is **continuous**.

2) If you **split** the **light** up with a **prism**, the **colours** all **merge** into each other — there **aren't** any **gaps** in the spectrum.

3) **Hot things** emit a **continuous spectrum** in the visible and infrared.

4) **All** the **wavelengths** are allowed because the electrons are **not confined** to **energy levels** in the object producing the **continuous spectrum**. The electrons are not bound to atoms and are **free**.

Decreasing wavelength ⟹

Cool Gases Remove Certain Wavelengths from the Continuous Spectrum

1) You get a **line absorption spectrum** when **light** with a **continuous spectrum** of **energy** (white light) passes through a cool gas.

2) At **low temperatures**, **most** of the **electrons** in the **gas atoms** will be in their **ground states**.

3) The electrons can only absorb **photons** with **energies** equal to the **difference** between **two energy levels**.

4) **Photons** of the **corresponding wavelengths** are **absorbed** by the **electrons** to **excite** them to **higher energy levels**.

5) These **wavelengths** are then **missing** from the **continuous spectrum** when it **comes out** the other side of the gas.

6) You see a **continuous spectrum** with **black lines** in it corresponding to the **absorbed wavelengths**.

7) If you **compare** the **absorption** and **emission spectra** of a **particular gas**, the **black lines** in the **absorption spectrum match up** to the **bright lines** in the **emission spectrum**.

Warm-Up Questions

Q1 Describe line absorption and line emission spectra. How are these two types of spectra produced?

Q2 Use the size of the energy level transitions involved to explain how the coating on a fluorescent tube converts UV into visible light.

PRACTICE QUESTIONS

Exam Question

Q1 An electron is accelerated through a potential difference of 12.1 V.

a) How much kinetic energy has it gained in i) eV and ii) joules? [2 marks]

b) This electron hits a hydrogen atom in its ground state and excites it.

   i) Explain what is meant by excitation. [1 mark]

   ii) Using the energy values on the right, calculate which energy level the electron from the hydrogen atom is excited to. [1 mark]

   iii) Calculate the energies of the three photons that might be emitted as the electron returns to its ground state. [3 marks]

$n = 5$	-0.54 eV
$n = 4$	-0.85 eV
$n = 3$	-1.5 eV
$n = 2$	-3.4 eV
$n = 1$	-13.6 eV

I can honestly say I've never got so excited that I've produced light...

This is heavy stuff. Quite interesting though, as I was just saying to Dom a moment ago. He's doing a psychology book. Psychology's probably quite interesting too — and easier. But it won't help you become an astrophysicist.

Wave-Particle Duality

Is it a wave? Is it a particle? No, it's a wave. No, it's a particle. No it's not, it's a wave. No, don't be daft, it's a particle.

Interference and Diffraction show Light as a Wave

1) Light produces **interference** and **diffraction** patterns — **alternating bands** of **dark** and **light**.

2) These can **only** be explained using **waves interfering constructively** (when two waves overlap in phase) or **interfering destructively** (when the two waves are out of phase). (See p.28.)

The Photoelectric Effect Shows Light Behaving as a Particle

1) **Einstein** explained the results of **photoelectricity experiments** (see p.16) by thinking of the **beam of light** as a series of **particle-like photons**.

2) If a **photon** of light is a **discrete** bundle of energy, then it can **interact** with an **electron** in a **one-to-one way**.

3) **All** the **energy** in the **photon** is **given** to one **electron**.

De Broglie Came Up with the Wave-Particle Duality Theory

1) Louis de Broglie made a **bold suggestion** in his **PhD thesis**:

> If 'wave-like' light showed **particle properties** (photons), 'particles' like **electrons** should be expected to show **wave-like properties**.

I'm not impressed —
this is just speculation.
What do you think, Dad?

2) The **de Broglie equation** relates a **wave property** (**wavelength, λ**) to a **moving particle property** (**momentum, *mv***). h = Planck's constant = 6.63×10^{-34} Js.

This is called the
de Broglie wavelength.
$$\lambda = \frac{h}{mv}$$

3) The **de Broglie wave** of a particle can be interpreted as a '**probability wave**'.
(The probability of finding a particle at a point is directly proportional to the square of the amplitude of the wave at that point — but you don't need to know that for your exam.)

4) Many physicists at the time **weren't very impressed** — his ideas were just **speculation**. But later experiments **confirmed** the wave nature of electrons.

Electron Diffraction shows the Wave Nature of Electrons

1) **Diffraction patterns** are observed when **accelerated electrons** in a vacuum tube **interact** with the **spaces** in a graphite **crystal**.

2) This **confirms** that electrons show **wave-like** properties.

3) According to wave theory, the **spread** of the **lines** in the diffraction pattern **increases** if the **wavelength** of the wave is **greater**.

4) In electron diffraction experiments, a **smaller accelerating voltage**, i.e. **slower** electrons, gives more **widely-spaced** rings.

5) **Increase** the **electron speed** (and therefore the electron **momentum**) and the diffraction pattern circles **squash together** towards the **middle**. This fits in with the **de Broglie** equation above — if the **momentum** is **greater**, the **wavelength** is **shorter** and the **spread** of the lines is **smaller**.

> In general, λ for electrons accelerated in a vacuum tube is about the same size as electromagnetic waves in the X-ray part of the spectrum.

6) If particles with a **greater mass** (e.g. **neutrons**) were travelling at the **same speed** as the electrons, they would show a more **tightly-packed diffraction pattern**. That's because a neutron's **mass** (and therefore its **momentum**) is **much greater** than an electron's, and so a neutron has a **shorter de Broglie wavelength**.

Wave-Particle Duality

Particles Don't show Wave-Like Properties All the Time

You **only** get **diffraction** if a particle interacts with an object of about the **same size** as its **de Broglie wavelength**. A **tennis ball**, for example, with **mass 0.058 kg** and **speed 100 ms^{-1}** has a **de Broglie wavelength** of **10^{-34} m**. That's **10^{19} times smaller** than the **nucleus** of an **atom**! There's nothing that small for it to interact with.

> **Example:** An electron of mass 9.11×10^{-31} kg is fired from an electron gun at 7.00×10^6 ms^{-1} (to 3 s.f.). What size object will the electron need to interact with in order to diffract?
>
> Momentum of electron = $mv = (9.11 \times 10^{-31}) \times (7.00 \times 10^6) = 6.377 \times 10^{-24}$ kg ms^{-1}
> $\lambda = h/mv = 6.63 \times 10^{-34} / 6.377 \times 10^{-24} = 1.0396... \times 10^{-10} = \mathbf{1.04 \times 10^{-10}}$ **m (to 3 s.f.)**
>
> Only crystals with atom layer spacing around this size are likely to cause the diffraction of this electron.

Wave-Particle Duality Wasn't Accepted Straight Away

De Broglie first **hypothesised** wave-particle duality to explain **observations** of light acting as both a particle and a wave. But his theory **wasn't accepted** straight away. **Other scientists** had to **evaluate** de Broglie's theory (by a process known as **peer review**) before he **published** it, and then it was **tested with experiments**. Once enough evidence was found to back it up, the theory was accepted as **validated** by the scientific community.

Scientists' understanding of the nature of matter has changed over time through this process of **hypothesis and validation**. De Broglie's theory is **accepted** to be true — that is, until any new conflicting evidence comes along.

Warm-Up Questions

Q1 Which observations show light to have a 'wave-like' character?

Q2 Which observations show light to have a 'particle' character?

Q3 What happens to the de Broglie wavelength of a particle if its momentum increases? How does this affect the particle's diffraction pattern?

Q4 Particle A has a de Broglie wavelength of 8×10^{-10} m and particle B has a de Broglie wavelength of 2×10^{-10} m. If the particles are travelling at the same speed, which particle has the greater mass?

Q5 Which observations show electrons to have a 'wave-like' character?

Exam Questions

Q1 a) State what is meant by the wave-particle nature of electromagnetic radiation. [1 mark]

    b) Calculate the momentum of an electron with a de Broglie wavelength of 590 nm. [2 marks]

Q2 Electrons travelling at a speed of 3.50×10^6 ms^{-1} exhibit wave properties.

    a) Calculate the wavelength of these electrons. (Mass of an electron = 9.11×10^{-31} kg) [2 marks]

    b) Calculate the speed of protons with the same wavelength as these electrons. (Mass of a proton = 1.67×10^{-27} kg) [2 marks]

    c) Some electrons and protons were accelerated from rest by the same potential difference, giving them the same kinetic energy. Explain why they will have different wavelengths. [3 marks]

Don't hide your wave-particles under a bushel...

Right — I think we'll all agree that quantum physics is a wee bit strange when you come to think about it. What it's saying is that electrons and photons aren't really waves, and they aren't really particles — they're both... at the same time. It's what quantum physicists like to call a 'juxtaposition of states'. Well they would, wouldn't they...

Extra Exam Practice

Well you've made it through <u>Sections 1 and 2</u>, so now it's time to put that grey matter to work again. Once you're confident you can recall quark compositions in your sleep, you're ready for these exam style questions linking all of the physics you've covered in Sections 1 and 2.

- Have a look at this example of how to answer a tricky exam question.
- Then check how much you've understood from Sections 1 and 2 by having a go at the questions on the next page.

Once you've mastered all the sections, there are synoptic questions covering the whole of AS/year 1 of A level on page 104.

---

1 The equation below shows the decay of a kaon. A π^0 particle decays after 8.4×10^{-17} s.

$$K^+ \rightarrow \pi^0 + e^+ + X$$

1.1 Identify particle X by applying the conservation laws for particle interactions.

(3 marks)

1.2 Suggest why it may be difficult to directly detect any of the products of this K^+ decay.

(3 marks)

1.1

Apply the conservation laws for baryon number, lepton number and charge:

Baryon number: $0 \rightarrow 0 + 0 + X$

So particle X must have a baryon number of 0 since baryon number is conserved.

L_e: $0 \rightarrow 0 + -1 + X$ so particle X must have $L_e = 1$ to conserve electron lepton number.

L_μ: $0 \rightarrow 0 + 0 + X$ so particle X must have $L_\mu = 0$.

To calculate the charge of each particle, split up the particles into quarks:

The quark composition of K^+ is up, anti-strange ($u\bar{s}$), so its charge is: $\frac{2}{3}e + \frac{1}{3}e = e$.

The quark composition of π^0 is up, anti-up ($u\bar{u}$) or down, anti-down ($d\bar{d}$), so its charge is either $\frac{2}{3}e - \frac{2}{3}e = 0$, or $-\frac{1}{3}e + \frac{1}{3}e = 0$. Either way, the charge of π^0 is 0.

So for charge: $e \rightarrow 0 + e + X$ so particle X must have a charge of 0 in order to conserve charge.

Particle X has no charge, a baryon number and muon lepton number of 0 and an electron lepton number of 1.
A particle with these properties is an electron neutrino.

You'd get 1 mark for applying the conservation laws to the baryon and lepton numbers correctly, 1 mark for showing that particle X has zero charge, and 1 mark for saying that particle X is an electron neutrino.

1.2

A positron may be difficult to detect because it will be **annihilated** very quickly when it meets an electron. An electron neutrino may be hard to detect because it is neutral and virtually massless. The π^0 particle decays extremely quickly, after only 8.4×10^{-17} s, so it may decay before it can be detected.

You'd get 1 mark for saying the positron will be annihilated, 1 mark for saying the electron neutrino has no charge and (virtually) no mass, and 1 mark for saying that the pion may decay too fast to be detected.

Remember you need to count electron and muon lepton numbers separately, see page 12.

The charges of the different quarks are on the data sheet. All the values are equal and opposite for antiquarks.

This part pulls together a few different topics. Think about what you know about each particle that could make it hard to detect.

Remember that kaons and pions are mesons, not baryons — this means that they have a baryon number of zero. The data sheet in the exam tells you which particles are baryons, mesons, or leptons.

It's easy to miss a particle when counting up each quantity. Be methodical and write everything down in a clear way so that you don't miss anything out.

Make sure you use the correct scientific terminology. It shows the examiner you know what you're talking about.

Extra Exam Practice

2   A student is researching the properties of aluminium.

2.1   The student finds the emission and absorption line spectra for aluminium.
Explain what the line spectra indicate about the structure of an atom.

(2 marks)

2.2   **Figure 1** shows how the stopping potential of photoelectrons emitted from aluminium varies with the frequency of incident light.

Use data from **Figure 1** to determine the work function of aluminium.
($e = 1.60 \times 10^{-19}$ C)

(3 marks)

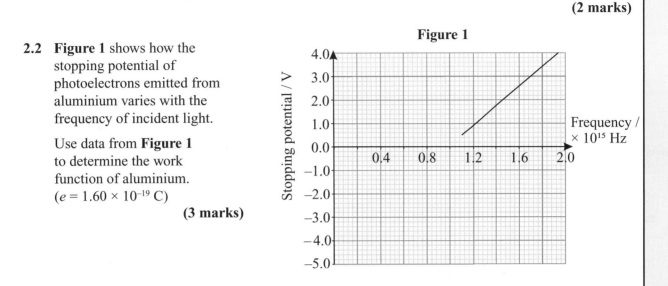

Figure 1

2.3   The student sets up an experiment in which electrons emitted from a sample of aluminium by the photoelectric effect are accelerated away from the sample by a potential difference. The sample is illuminated with light of frequency 2.10×10^{15} Hz. Determine the accelerating potential difference required for the emitted photoelectrons to have a minimum de Broglie wavelength of 415 pm.
($h = 6.63 \times 10^{-34}$ Js, $m_e = 9.11 \times 10^{-31}$ kg)

(5 marks)

3   Read the passage below and answer the following questions.

Neutrinos are fundamental particles that are difficult to detect. Neutrinos were first theorised to exist in the 1930s, and discovered in 1956 by the Cowan-Reines neutrino experiment. In the experiment a nuclear reactor was surrounded with water tanks. Beta-minus decays inside the reactor produced antineutrinos which interacted with the

5   protons in water, creating positrons. Gamma rays produced by the annihilation of these positrons and nearby electrons were then detected using a series of scintillators and photomultiplier tubes. Photomultiplier tubes are very sensitive photon detectors that make use of the photoelectric effect when photons hit a surface.

3.1   The interaction between an antineutrino and a proton (line 4) produces a second decay product besides a positron. Write a possible decay equation for this process. Explain your answer.

(3 marks)

3.2   Calculate the minimum frequency of the gamma rays produced (line 5).
(Rest energy of an electron = 0.511 MeV, $e = 1.60 \times 10^{-19}$ C, $h = 6.63 \times 10^{-34}$ Js)

(2 marks)

3.3   Photomultiplier tubes (line 7) can't detect photons with wavelengths longer than a certain value. Suggest why this is the case.

(2 marks)

Progressive Waves

Aaaah... playing with long springs and waggling ropes about. It's all good clean fun as my mate Richard used to say...

A **Wave** is the **Oscillation** of **Particles** or **Fields**

A **progressive** (moving) wave carries **energy** from one place to another **without transferring any material**.
A wave is caused by something making particles or fields oscillate (or vibrate) at a source.
These oscillations pass through the medium (or field) as the wave travels, carrying energy with it.

Here are some ways you can tell waves carry energy:

1) Electromagnetic waves cause things to **heat up**.
2) **X-rays** and **gamma rays** knock electrons out of their orbits, causing **ionisation**.
3) Loud **sounds** cause large oscillations of air particles which can make things **vibrate**.
4) **Wave power** can be used to **generate electricity**.
5) Since waves carry energy away, the **source** of the wave **loses energy**.

Alex loved wave power.

You Need to Know These **Bits** of a **Wave**

1) **Cycle** — one **complete vibration** of the wave.
2) **Displacement**, *x*, metres — how far a **point** on the wave has **moved** from its **undisturbed position.**
3) **Amplitude**, *A*, metres — **maximum magnitude** of **displacement**.
4) **Wavelength**, λ, metres — the **length** of **one whole wave cycle**, from **crest** to **crest** or **trough** to **trough**.

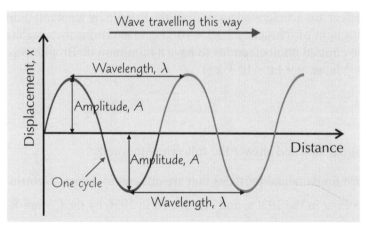

5) **Period**, *T*, seconds — the **time taken** for a **whole cycle** (vibration) to complete, or to pass a given point.
6) **Frequency**, *f*, hertz — the **number** of **cycles** (vibrations) **per second** passing a given **point**.
7) **Phase** — a measurement of the **position** of a certain **point** along the wave cycle.
8) **Phase difference** — the amount one wave lags behind another.

Phase and phase difference are measured in **angles** (in degrees or radians) or as **fractions of a cycle** (see p.28).

Waves Can Be **Reflected** and **Refracted**

Reflection — the wave is **bounced back** when it **hits a boundary**. E.g. you can see the reflection of
light in mirrors. The reflection of water waves can be demonstrated in a ripple tank.

Refraction — the wave **changes direction** as it enters a **different medium**.
The change in direction is a result of the wave slowing down or speeding up.

The **Frequency** is the **Inverse** of the **Period**

$$\text{Frequency} = \frac{1}{\text{Period}}$$

$$f = \frac{1}{T}$$

It's that simple.
Get the **units** straight: **1 Hz = 1 s^{-1}**.

Progressive Waves

The **Wave Equation** Links **Wave Speed, Frequency** and **Wavelength**

Wave speed can be measured just like the speed of anything else:

$$\text{Wave speed } (c) = \frac{\text{Distance travelled } (d)}{\text{Time taken } (t)}$$

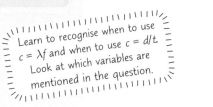
*Remember, you're not measuring how fast a physical point (like one molecule of rope) moves. You're measuring how fast a point on the **wave pattern** moves.*

From this you can get to the **wave equation**, which you've seen before on p.6.

$$\text{Speed of wave } (c) = \text{wavelength } (\lambda) \times \text{frequency } (f) \qquad \boxed{c = \lambda f}$$

You get to the wave equation because a wave travels λ m in T seconds and $f = 1/T$.

Example: A wave has a wavelength of 420 m and travels at a speed of 125 ms⁻¹.
Find the frequency of this wave.

Just rearrange the wave equation, to find f.

$$c = \lambda f \quad \text{so} \quad f = \frac{c}{\lambda} = \frac{125}{420} = 0.2976... = \textbf{0.30 Hz (to 2 s.f.)}$$

Learn to recognise when to use $c = \lambda f$ and when to use $c = d/t$. Look at which variables are mentioned in the question.

The lowest no. of significant figures the question data is given to is 2 s.f.,
so give your answer to the same amount of significant figures.

You may have seen c used before as the **speed of light** in a vacuum. Light is a type of electromagnetic wave. All EM waves travel with a **constant speed** in a **vacuum** of $c = 3.00 \times 10^8$ ms⁻¹. The c used in the wave equation is the speed of the **wave in question** — it can take **any** value depending on the wave.

Warm-Up Questions

Q1 Does a wave carry matter **or** energy from one place to another?
Q2 Write down the relationship between the frequency of a wave and its time period.
Q3 Give the units of frequency, displacement and amplitude.
Q4 Write down the equation connecting c, λ and f.

PRACTICE QUESTIONS

Exam Questions

Q1 A buoy floating on the sea takes 6.0 seconds to rise and fall once (complete a full cycle). The difference in height between the buoy at its lowest and highest points is 1.2 m, and waves pass it at a speed of 3.0 ms⁻¹.

a) Calculate the wavelength. [2 marks]

b) State the amplitude of the waves. [1 mark]

Q2 Light travelling through a vacuum has a wavelength of 7.1×10^{-7} m. Calculate its frequency. [1 mark]

Q3 Which of the following statements is correct? [1 mark]

A	Progressive waves transfer energy by transferring material.
B	Progressive waves transfer energy by oscillating particles/fields.
C	The source of a progressive wave has a constant energy.
D	Light is faster than other EM waves in a vacuum.

Hope you haven't phased out...

This isn't too difficult to start you off — most of it you'll have done at GCSE anyway. But once again, it's a whole lot of definitions and a handy equation to remember, and you won't get far without learning them. Yada yada.

Longitudinal and Transverse Waves

There are different types of wave — the difference is easiest to see using a long spring. Try it — you'll have hours of fun.

Transverse Waves Vibrate at Right Angles to the Direction of Energy Transfer

All **electromagnetic** waves are **transverse**. They travel as vibrating magnetic and electric **fields** — with vibrations **perpendicular** to the direction of **energy transfer**. Other examples of transverse waves are **ripples** on water or waves on **strings**.

There are **two** main ways of **drawing** transverse waves:

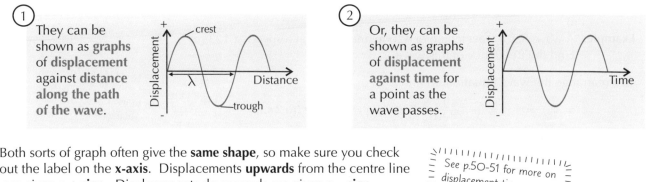

① They can be shown as **graphs** of **displacement** against **distance** along the path of the wave.

② Or, they can be shown as graphs of **displacement** against **time** for a point as the wave passes.

Both sorts of graph often give the **same shape**, so make sure you check out the label on the **x-axis**. Displacements **upwards** from the centre line are given a **+ sign**. Displacements downwards are given a **– sign**.

See p.50-51 for more on displacement-time graphs.

Longitudinal Waves Vibrate Along the Direction of Energy Transfer

The most common example of a **longitudinal wave** is **sound**. A sound wave consists of alternate **compressions** and **rarefactions** of the **medium** it's travelling through. (That's why sound can't go through a vacuum.) Some types of earthquake shock waves are also longitudinal.

It's hard to **represent** longitudinal waves **graphically**. You'll usually see them plotted as **displacement** against **time**. These can be **confusing** though, because they look like a **transverse wave**.

A Polarised Wave Only Oscillates in One Direction

1) If you **shake a rope** to make a **wave** you can move your hand **up and down** or **side to side** or in a **mixture** of directions — it still makes a **transverse wave**.

2) But if you try to pass **waves in a rope** through a **vertical fence**, the wave will only get through if the **vibrations** are **vertical**. The fence filters out vibration in other directions. This is called **polarising** the wave.

Polarisation **can only happen** for **transverse** waves.

Longitudinal and Transverse Waves

Polarisation is Evidence that Electromagnetic Waves are Transverse

In 1808, Etienne-Louis Malus discovered that light was **polarised** by reflection. Physicists at the time thought that light spread like sound, as a **longitudinal** wave, so they struggled to explain polarisation. In 1817, Young suggested light was a **transverse** wave consisting of vibrating electric and magnetic **fields** at right angles to the transfer of energy. This explained why light could be **polarised**.

Polarising Filters Only Transmit Vibrations in One Direction

1) Ordinary **light waves** are a mixture of **different directions** of **vibration**. (The things vibrating are electric and magnetic fields.) They can be **polarised** using a **polarising filter**.

2) If you have two polarising filters at **right angles** to each other, then **no** light will get through.

3) Light becomes **partially** polarised when reflected from some surfaces — some of it vibrates in the **same direction**.

Unpolarised light

Polarising filters

Transmission axes (light vibrating this way gets through)

Direction of vibrations

4) If you view reflected partially polarised light through a polarising filter at the correct angle you can block out unwanted **glare**. **Polaroid sunglasses** make use of this effect.

Television and Radio Signals are Polarised

If you walk down the street and look up at the **TV aerials** on people's houses, you'll see that the **rods** (the sticky-out bits) on them are all **horizontal**. The reason for this is that **TV signals** are **polarised** by the orientation of the **rods** on the **broadcasting aerial**. To receive a strong signal, you have to **line up** the **rods** on the **receiving aerial** with the **rods** on the **transmitting aerial** — if they aren't aligned, the signal strength will be lower.

It's the **same** with **radio** — if you try **tuning a radio** and then **moving** the **aerial** around, your signal will **come and go** as the transmitting and receiving aerials go in and out of **alignment**.

The rods on this broadcasting aerial are horizontal.

Warm-Up Questions

Q1 Give an example of a transverse wave and a longitudinal wave.

Q2 What is a polarised wave?

Q3 How can you polarise light?

Q4 Why do you have to line up transmitting and receiving television aerials?

Exam Questions

Q1 Sunlight reflected from road surfaces mostly vibrates in one direction.

a) Explain how this is evidence that sunlight is made up of transverse waves. [2 marks]

b) Explain how Polaroid sunglasses help to reduce glare caused by reflections. [2 marks]

Q2 Explain why sound waves cannot be polarised. [2 marks]

So many waves — my arms are getting tired...

Right, there's lots to learn on these two pages, so I won't hold you up with chat. Don't panic though — a lot of this stuff will be familiar from GCSE, so it's not like you're starting from scratch. One last thing — I know television is on this page, but it doesn't mean you can tune in and call it revision — it won't help. Get the revision done, then take a break.

Superposition and Coherence

When two waves get together, it can be either really impressive or really disappointing.

Superposition Happens When Two or More Waves Pass Through Each Other

1) At the **instant** the waves **cross**, the **displacements** due to each wave **combine**. Then **each wave** goes on its merry way. You can **see** this if **two pulses** are sent **simultaneously** from each end of a rope.

2) The **principle of superposition** says that when two or more **waves cross**, the **resultant** displacement equals the **vector sum** of the **individual** displacements.

BEFORE	MEETING	AFTER

'Superposition' means 'one thing on top of another thing'. You can use the same idea in reverse — a complex wave can be separated out mathematically into several simple sine waves of various sizes.

Interference can be Constructive or Destructive

1) A **crest** plus a **crest** gives a **bigger crest**. A **trough** plus a **trough** gives a **bigger trough**. These are both examples of **constructive interference**.

2) A **crest** plus a **trough** of **equal size** gives... nothing. The two displacements **cancel each other out** completely. This is called **destructive interference**.

3) If the **crest** and the **trough** aren't the **same size**, then the destructive interference isn't **total**. For the interference to be **noticeable**, the two **amplitudes** should be **nearly equal**.

Graphically, you can superimpose waves by adding the individual displacements at each point along the x-axis, and then plotting them.

In Phase Means In Step — Two Points In Phase Interfere Constructively

1) Two points on a wave are **in phase** if they are both at the **same point** in the **wave cycle**. Points in phase have the **same displacement** and **velocity**.

   On the graph below, points **A** and **B** are **in phase**; points **A** and **C** are **out of phase**.

2) It's mathematically **handy** to show one **complete cycle** of a wave as an **angle of 360° (2π radians)**.

To convert from degrees to radians, multiply by π/180°.
To convert from radians to degrees, multiply by 180°/π.

Displacement

position

360°   720°

A   B

C

3) **Two points** with a **phase difference** of **zero** or a **multiple of 360°** (i.e. a **full cycle**) are **in phase**.

4) **Points** with a **phase difference** of **odd-number multiples of 180°** (π **radians**, or a **half cycle**) are **exactly out of phase**.

5) You can also talk about two **different waves** being **in phase**. **In practice** this happens because **both** waves came from the **same oscillator**. In **other** situations there will nearly always be a **phase difference** between two waves.

Superposition and Coherence

To Get Interference Patterns the Two Sources Must Be Coherent

Interference **still happens** when you're observing waves of **different wavelength** and **frequency** — but it happens in a **jumble**. In order to get clear **interference patterns**, the two or more sources must be **coherent**.

Two sources are **coherent** if they have the **same wavelength** and **frequency** and a **fixed phase difference** between them.

In exam questions, the 'fixed phase difference' is almost certainly going to be zero. The two sources will be in phase.

Constructive or Destructive Interference Depends on the Path Difference

1) Whether you get **constructive** or **destructive** interference at a **point** depends on how **much further one wave** has travelled than the **other wave** to get to that point.

2) The **amount** by which the path travelled by one wave is **longer** than the path travelled by the other wave is called the **path difference**.

3) At **any point an equal distance** from two **coherent** and **in phase** sources, you will get **constructive interference**. You also get constructive interference at any point where the **path difference** is a **whole number of wavelengths**. At these points the two waves are **in phase** and **reinforce** each other. But at points where the path difference is **half a wavelength**, **one and a half** wavelengths, **two and a half** wavelengths etc., the waves arrive **out of phase** and you get **destructive interference**.

You could use a microphone and an oscilloscope to investigate how interference varies with position along this line.

Constructive interference occurs when:

path difference $= n\lambda$ (where n is an integer)

Destructive interference occurs when:

path difference $= \dfrac{(2n+1)\lambda}{2} = (n + \frac{1}{2})\lambda$

Warm-Up Questions

Q1 Why does the principle of superposition deal with the **vector** sum of two displacements?
Q2 What happens when a crest meets a slightly smaller trough?
Q3 What is meant by the path difference of two waves?
Q4 If two points on a wave have a phase difference of 1440°, are they in phase?

Exam Questions

Q1 a) Two wave sources are coherent. Explain what this means. [2 marks]

b) Explain why you might have difficulty in observing interference patterns in an area affected by two waves from two sources even though the two sources are coherent. [1 mark]

Q2 Two points on a wave are exactly out of phase. Which row of the table correctly compares the two points? [1 mark]

	Phase Difference	Velocities	Displacements
A	180°	Equal	Opposite
B	180°	Opposite	Opposite
C	360°	Equal	Equal
D	360°	Opposite	Opposite

Learn this and you'll be in a super position to pass your exam...   ...I'll get my coat.

There are a few really crucial concepts here: a) interference can be constructive or destructive, b) constructive interference happens when the path difference is a whole number of wavelengths, c) the sources must be coherent.

Stationary Waves

Stationary waves are weird things — they move but they don't actually go anywhere.

Progressive Waves Reflected at a Boundary Can Create a Stationary Wave

> A stationary (standing) wave is the **superposition** of **two progressive waves**
> with the **same frequency (wavelength)**, moving in **opposite directions**.

1) Unlike progressive waves, **no energy** is transmitted by a stationary wave.

2) You can demonstrate stationary waves by setting up a **driving oscillator** at one end of a **stretched string** with the other end fixed. The wave generated by the oscillator is **reflected** back and forth.

3) For most frequencies the resultant **pattern** is a **jumble**. However, if the oscillator happens to produce an **exact number of waves** in the time it takes for a wave to get to the **end** and **back again**, then the **original** and **reflected** waves **reinforce** each other.

4) At these **"resonant frequencies"** you get a **stationary wave** where the **pattern doesn't move** — it just sits there, bobbing up and down. Happy, at peace with the world...

A sitting wave.

Stationary Waves in Strings Form Oscillating "Loops" Separated by Nodes

Each particle vibrates at **right angles** to the string.

Nodes are where the **amplitude** of the vibration is **zero**. **Antinodes** are points of **maximum amplitude**.

At resonant frequencies, an **exact number** of **half wavelengths** fits onto the string:

First Harmonic

This stationary wave is vibrating at the **lowest possible** resonant frequency. It has one "loop" with a **node at each end**.

Node — Node — Half a wavelength (½λ) — Oscillator

Second Harmonic

This is the **second harmonic**. It is **twice** the frequency of the **first harmonic**. There are **two** "loops" with a **node** in the **middle** and **one at each end**.

Node — Node — Node — λ — Oscillator

Third Harmonic

The **third harmonic** is **three times** the frequency of the first harmonic. **1½ wavelengths** fit on the string.

Node — Node — Node — Node — 1½λ — Oscillator

You can Demonstrate Stationary Waves with Microwaves and Sounds

Microwaves Reflected Off a Metal Plate Set Up a Stationary Wave

Microwave stationary wave apparatus

You can find the **nodes** and **antinodes** by moving the **probe** between the **transmitter** and **reflecting plate**.

metal plate — probe — microwave transmitter — to meter or loudspeaker

Powder Can Show Stationary Waves in a Tube of Air

Stationary **sound** waves are produced in the **glass tube**.

The lycopodium **powder** (don't worry, you don't need to know what that is) laid along the bottom of the tube is **shaken away** from the **antinodes** but left **undisturbed** at the **nodes**.

loudspeaker — glass tube — lycopodium powder — to signal generator

Stationary Waves

You Can Investigate **Factors** Affecting the **Resonant Frequencies** of a String

string fixed to
vibration transducer

length, *l*

pulley

signal generator

string

bench

masses

tension, *T*

A vibration transducer is connected to a signal generator that tells it the frequency of the wave you want. A vibrating plate on the transducer creates the wave.

1) Start by measuring the **mass** (*M*) and **length** (*L*) of strings of different types using a **mass balance** and a ruler. Then find the **mass per unit length** of each string (*μ*) using:

$$\mu = \frac{M}{L}$$ The units of *μ* are kgm⁻¹

2) Set up the apparatus shown in the diagram with one of your strings. Record *μ*, measure and record the **length** (*l*) and work out the **tension** (*T*) using:

$$T = mg$$ where *m* is the total mass of the masses in kg

3) Turn on the **signal generator** and vary the frequency until you find the **first harmonic** — i.e. a stationary wave that has a **node** at each end and a single **antinode**. This is the **frequency** of the first harmonic, *f*.

Then investigate how the **length, tension** or **mass per unit length** of the string affects the **resonant frequency** by:

1) Keeping the string **type** (*μ*) and the **tension** (*T*) in it the same and altering the **length** (*l*). Do this by moving the **vibration transducer** towards or away from the pulley. Find the **first harmonic** again, and record *f* against *l*.

2) Keeping the string **type** (*μ*) and **length** (*l*) the same and **adding** or **removing masses** to change the tension (*T*). Find the first harmonic again and record *f* against *T*.

3) Keeping the **length** (*l*) and **tension** (*T*) the same, but using **different string** samples to vary *μ*. Find the first harmonic and record *f* against *μ*.

You can do all of this with a different harmonic — just remember to use the same one throughout the experiment so you're comparing the same resonant frequency.

You should find the following from your investigation:

1) The **longer** the string, the **lower** the resonant frequency
   — because the **half wavelength** at the resonant frequency is longer.

2) The **heavier** (i.e. the more mass per unit length) the string, the **lower** the resonant frequency — because waves travel more **slowly** down the string. For a given **length** a **lower** wave speed, *c*, makes a **lower** frequency, *f*.

3) The **looser** the string the **lower** the resonant frequency — because waves travel more **slowly** down a **loose** string.

The **frequency** of the first harmonic, *f*, is: $f = \frac{1}{2l}\sqrt{\frac{T}{\mu}}$ Where *l* is the string length in m, *T* is the tension in the string and *μ* is the mass per unit length of the string.

Warm-Up Questions

Q1 How do stationary waves form?

Q2 At four times the frequency of the first harmonic, how many half wavelengths would fit on a violin string?

Q3 Describe an experiment to investigate stationary waves in a column of air.

Q4 How does the displacement of a particle at one antinode compare to that of a particle at another antinode?

Exam Question

Q1 A stationary wave at the first harmonic frequency, 10 Hz (to 2 s.f.), is formed on a stretched string of length 1.2 m.

a) Calculate the wavelength of the wave.   [2 marks]

b) The tension is doubled whilst all other factors remain constant. The frequency is adjusted to once more find the first harmonic of the string. Calculate the new frequency of the first harmonic.   [3 marks]

c) Explain how the variation of amplitude along the string differs from that of a progressive wave.   [2 marks]

Don't get tied up in knots...

Just remember that two progressive waves can combine to make a stationary wave. How many nodes there are shows what harmonic it is (e.g. 2 nodes = 1st harmonic), and you can change its frequency by changing the medium its in.

Diffraction

This page is essentially about shining light through small gaps and creating pretty patterns. Aaaahh look, a rainbow.

Waves Go **Round Corners** and **Spread** Out of **Gaps**

The way that **waves spread out** as they come through a **narrow gap** or go round obstacles is called **diffraction**. **All** waves diffract, but it's not always easy to observe.

The **amount** of diffraction depends on the **wavelength** of the wave compared with the **size of the gap**.

1) When the gap is **a lot bigger** than the **wavelength**, diffraction is **unnoticeable**.

2) You get **noticeable diffraction** through a gap **several** wavelengths wide.

3) You get the **most** diffraction when the gap is **the same** size as the **wavelength**.

4) If the gap is **smaller** than the wavelength, the waves are mostly just **reflected back**.

When sound passes through a doorway, the size of gap and the wavelength are usually roughly equal, so a lot of diffraction occurs. That's why you have no trouble hearing someone through an open door to the next room, even if the other person is out of your line of sight. The reason that you can't see him or her is that when light passes through the doorway, it is passing through a gap around a hundred million times bigger than its wavelength — the amount of diffraction is tiny. So to get noticeable diffraction with light, you must shine it through a very narrow slit.

Light Shone Through a **Narrow Slit** Can Form a **Diffraction Pattern**

To observe a clear **diffraction pattern** for light, you need to use a **monochromatic**, **coherent** light source. Monochromatic just means all the light has the same **wavelength** (and frequency) and so is the same **colour**. **Lasers** are a monochromatic and coherent light source.

Demonstrating Light Diffraction Patterns with a Laser

If the wavelength of light is about the **same size** as the aperture, you get a diffraction pattern.

You'll see a **central bright fringe** (central maximum), with dark and bright fringes **alternating** on either side. The dark and bright fringes are caused by **destructive** and **constructive interference** of light waves (see p.28).

Diffracted **White Light** Creates **Spectra** of Colours

1) **White light** is actually a **mixture** of different colours, each with different **wavelengths**.

2) When white light is shone through a single narrow slit, all of the different wavelengths are **diffracted** by different amounts.

3) This means that **instead** of getting clear **fringes** (as you would with a **monochromatic** light source) you get **spectra** of colours.

Diffraction

Intensity of Light Means Number of Photons

1) The **central maximum** in a single slit light diffraction pattern is the **brightest** part of the pattern.

2) This is because the **intensity** of light is highest in the centre.

3) **Intensity** is the **power per unit area**.

4) For monochromatic light, all photons have the **same energy**, so an increase in the intensity means an increase in the **number of photons per second**.

5) So there are **more photons** per **unit area** hitting the central maximum per second than the other bright fringes.

Fred wasn't sure about his fringe intensity.

See p.16 for the photon model of light.

The Width of the Central Maximum Varies with Wavelength and Slit Size

When light is shone through a single slit, there are **two** things which affect the **width** of the central maximum:

1) **Increasing** the **slit width** decreases the amount of diffraction. This means the central maximum is narrower, and the **intensity** of the central maximum is **higher**.

2) **Increasing** the **wavelength** increases the amount of diffraction. This means the central maximum is wider, and the intensity of the central maximum is **lower**.

Warm-Up Questions

Q1 What is diffraction?

Q2 Do all waves diffract?

Q3 a) Sketch the pattern produced when monochromatic light is shone through a narrow slit onto a screen.

b) If the wavelength of the monochromatic light was decreased, what would happen to the central maximum?

Q4 What would you expect to see when white light is shone through a thin slit onto a screen?

Q5 What happens to the number of photons in a light beam if the intensity increases?

Exam Questions

Q1 A fire alarm can be heard from the next room through a doorway, even though it is not in the line of sight. Explain why this happens, with reference to the wavelengths of sound and light waves. [3 marks]

Q2 A student shines a laser beam through a narrow slit onto a screen.

a) State and explain one reason why using laser light produces a clearer diffraction pattern than other light sources. [2 marks]

b) The student uses a narrower slit. Describe how this will affect the central maximum of the diffraction pattern. Explain your answer. [3 marks]

Waves are just like me at the weekend — they like to spread out...

An important point to remember is that diffraction's only noticeable when the wavelength is roughly equal to the size of the gap the wave is going through. Different light sources give different patterns when diffracted, make sure you know this and can explain why it happens. Diffraction crops up again in physics — so make sure you really understand it.

Two-Source Interference

You know what happens with one light source, so now it's time to see what happens with two. I can hardly wait...

Demonstrating **Two-Source** Interference in **Water** and **Sound** is Easy

1) It's **easy** to demonstrate **two-source interference** for either **sound** or **water** because they've got **wavelengths** of a handy **size** that you can **measure**.

2) You need **coherent** sources, which means the **wavelength** and **frequency** have to be the **same**. The trick is to use the **same oscillator** to drive **both sources**. For **water**, one **vibrator drives two dippers**. For sound, **one oscillator** is connected to **two loudspeakers**. (See diagram on page 29.)

Demonstrating **Two-Source** Interference for **Light** is Harder

Young's Double-Slit Experiment

1) To see two-source interference with light, you can either use two separate, coherent light sources or you can shine a laser through two slits. Laser light is coherent and monochromatic.

2) Young's double-slit experiment shines a laser through two slits onto a screen.

3) The slits have to be about the same size as the wavelength of the laser light so that it is diffracted — then the light from the slits acts like two coherent point sources.

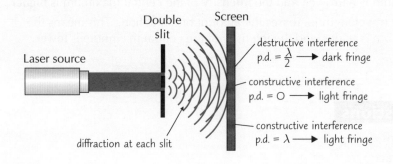

Laser source

Double slit

Screen

destructive interference
p.d. = $\frac{\lambda}{2}$ → dark fringe

constructive interference
p.d. = 0 → light fringe

constructive interference
p.d. = λ → light fringe

diffraction at each slit

4) You get a pattern of light and dark fringes, depending on whether constructive or destructive interference is taking place. Thomas Young — the first person to do this experiment (with a lamp rather than a laser) — came up with an equation to work out the wavelength of the light from this experiment (see p.35).

Working with lasers is very **dangerous** because laser light is focused into a very direct, powerful beam of monochromatic light. If you looked at a laser beam **directly**, your eye's lens would focus it onto your retina, which would be **permanently damaged**.

To make sure you don't cause damage while using lasers, you should:

1) Never shine the laser towards a person.
2) Wear laser safety goggles.
3) Avoid shining the laser beam at a reflective surface.
4) Have a warning sign on display.
5) Turn the laser off when it's not needed.

You Can Do a Similar Experiment with Microwaves

To see interference patterns with **microwaves**, you can **replace** the laser and slits with two microwave **transmitter cones** attached to the **same** signal generator.

You also need to replace the screen with a microwave **receiver probe** (like the one used in the stationary waves experiment on page 30).

If you move the probe along the path of the green arrow, you'll get an **alternating pattern** of **strong** and **weak** signals — just like the light and dark fringes on the screen.

microwave generator

probe

Two-Source Interference

Work Out the Wavelength with Young's Double-Slit Formula

1) The fringe spacing (w), wavelength (λ), spacing between slits (s) and the distance from slits to screen (D) are all related by **Young's double-slit formula**, which works for all waves.

$$\text{Fringe spacing, } w = \frac{\lambda D}{s}$$

'Fringe spacing' means the distance from the centre of one minimum to the centre of the next minimum or from the centre of one maximum to the centre of the next maximum.

Always check your fringe spacing.

2) Since the wavelength of light is so small you can see from the formula that a high ratio of D / s is needed to make the fringe spacing **big enough to see**.

3) Rearranging, you can use $\lambda = ws / D$ to **calculate the wavelength** of light.

4) The fringes are **so tiny** that it's very hard to get an **accurate value of w**. It's easier to measure across **several** fringes then **divide** by the number of **fringe widths** between them.

Young's Experiment was Evidence for the Wave Nature of EM Radiation

1) Towards the end of the **17th century**, two important **theories of light** were published — one by Isaac Newton and the other by a chap called Huygens. **Newton's** theory suggested that light was made up of tiny particles, which he called "**corpuscles**". And **Huygens** put forward a theory using **waves**.

2) The **corpuscular theory** could explain **reflection** and **refraction**, but **diffraction** and **interference** are both **uniquely** wave properties. If it could be **shown** that light showed interference patterns, that would help settle the argument once and for all.

3) **Young's** double-slit experiment (over 100 years later) provided the necessary evidence. It showed that light could both **diffract** (through the narrow slits) and **interfere** (to form the interference pattern on the screen).

   Of course, this being Physics, nothing's ever simple — give it another 100 years or so and the debate would be raging again, (p.16).

Warm-Up Questions

Q1 In Young's experiment, why do you get a bright fringe at a point equidistant from both slits?

Q2 What does Young's experiment show about the nature of light?

Q3 Write down Young's double-slit formula.

PRACTICE QUESTIONS

Exam Questions

Q1 a) The diagram on the right shows two coherent light sources, S_1 and S_2, being shone on a screen. State the measurements you would need to take to calculate the wavelength of the light. [3 marks]

b) S_1 and S_2 may be slits in a screen behind which there is a source of laser light, instead of being two separate sources. State two safety precautions you should take when using this set-up. Explain your answer. [2 marks]

screen

S_1

S_2

Q2 In an experiment to study sound interference, two loudspeakers are connected to an oscillator emitting sound at 1320 Hz and set up as shown in the diagram. They are 1.5 m apart and 7.3 m away from the line AC. A listener moving along the line hears minimum sound at A, maximum sound at B and minimum sound again at C. (You may assume that Young's double-slit formula can be used in this calculation).

Oscillator — 1.5 m — 7.3 m →

A
B
C

a) Calculate the wavelength of the sound waves if the speed of sound in air is taken to be 330 ms⁻¹. [1 mark]

b) Calculate the separation of points A and C. [1 mark]

Learn this stuff — or you'll be playing ketchup...

A few things to learn here — some diffraction experiments, a formula and a little bit of history. Be careful when you're calculating the fringe width by averaging over several fringes. Don't just divide by the number of bright lines. Ten bright lines will only have nine fringe widths between them, not ten. It's an easy mistake to make, but you have been warned.

Diffraction Gratings

Ay... starting to get into some pretty funky stuff now. I like light experiments.

Interference Patterns Get **Sharper** When You Diffract Through **More Slits**

1) You can repeat **Young's double-slit** experiment (see p.34) with **more than two equally spaced** slits. You get basically the **same shaped** pattern as for two slits — but the **bright bands** are **brighter** and **narrower** and the **dark areas** between are **darker**.

2) When **monochromatic light** (one wavelength) is passed through a **grating** with **hundreds** of slits per millimetre, the interference pattern is **really sharp** because there are so **many beams reinforcing** the **pattern**.

3) Sharper fringes make for more **accurate** measurements.

screen

diffraction grating

Monochromatic Light on a **Diffraction Grating** gives **Sharp Lines**

1) For **monochromatic** light, all the maxima are sharp lines. (It's different for white light — see page 32.)

2) There's a line of **maximum brightness** at the centre called the **zero order** line.

3) The lines just **either side** of the central one are called **first order lines**. The **next pair out** are called **second order** lines and so on.

4) For a grating with slits a distance *d* apart, the angle between the **incident beam** and **the nth order maximum** is given by:

$$d \sin \theta = n\lambda$$

5) So by observing *d*, *θ* and *n* you can **calculate the wavelength** of the light.

3rd order (*n* = 3)
2nd order (*n* = 2)
1st order (*n* = 1)
zero order
1st order (*n* = 1)
2nd order (*n* = 2)
3rd order (*n* = 3)

grating with slits *d* apart

light of wavelength *λ*

If the grating has N slits per metre, then the slit spacing, d, is just 1/N metres.

DERIVING THE EQUATION:

1) At **each slit**, the incoming waves are **diffracted**. These diffracted waves then **interfere** with each other to produce an **interference pattern**.

2) Consider the **first order maximum**. This happens at the **angle** when the waves from one slit line up with waves from the **next slit** that are **exactly one wavelength** behind.

Direction of 1st order wavefronts

3) Call the **angle** between the **first order maximum** and the **incoming light** *θ*.

4) Now, look at the **triangle** highlighted in the diagram. The angle is *θ* (using basic geometry), *d* is the slit spacing and the **path difference** is *λ*.

5) So, for the first maximum, using trig:
$$d \sin \theta = \lambda$$

6) The other maxima occur when the path difference is 2*λ*, 3*λ*, 4*λ*, etc. So to make the equation **general**, just replace *λ* with *nλ*, where *n* is an integer — the **order** of the maximum.

Diffraction Gratings

You can Draw **General Conclusions** from $d \sin \theta = n\lambda$

1) If λ is bigger, $\sin \theta$ is bigger, and so θ is bigger. This means that the larger the wavelength, the more the pattern will spread out.

2) If d is bigger, $\sin \theta$ is smaller. This means that the coarser the grating, the less the pattern will spread out.

3) Values of $\sin \theta$ greater than 1 are impossible. So if for a certain n you get a result of more than 1 for $\sin \theta$ you know that that order doesn't exist.

Diffraction Gratings Help to Identify **Elements** and Calculate **Atomic Spacing**

1) **White light** is really a **mixture** of **colours**. If you **diffract** white light through a **grating** then the patterns due to **different wavelengths** within the white light are **spread out** by **different** amounts.

2) Each **order** in the pattern becomes a **spectrum**, with **red** on the **outside** and **violet** on the **inside**. The **zero order maximum** stays **white** because all the wavelengths just pass straight through.

3) **Astronomers** and **chemists** often need to study spectra to help identify elements. They use diffraction gratings rather than prisms because they're **more accurate**.

| second order | first order | zero order (white) | first order | second order |

4) The wavelength of **X-rays** is of a similar scale to the spacing between **atoms** in crystalline solids. This means that X-rays will form a **diffraction pattern** when directed at a thin crystal.

5) The crystal acts like a **diffraction grating** and the spacing between **atoms** (slit width) can be found from the diffraction pattern.

6) This is called **X-ray crystallography** — it was used to discover the structure of **DNA**.

Warm-Up Questions

Q1 How is the diffraction grating pattern for white light different from the pattern for laser light?

Q2 What difference does it make to the pattern if you use a finer grating?

Q3 What equation is used to find the angle between the nth order maximum and the incident beam for a diffraction grating?

Q4 Derive the equation you quoted in Q3.

Exam Questions

Q1 Yellow laser light of wavelength 6.0×10^{-7} m is transmitted through a diffraction grating of 4.0×10^5 lines per metre.

a) Calculate the angle to the normal at which the first and second order bright lines are seen. [3 marks]

b) State whether there is a fifth order line. Explain your answer. [1 mark]

Q2 Visible, monochromatic light is transmitted through a diffraction grating of 3.7×10^5 lines per metre. The first order maximum is at an angle of 14.2° to the incident beam. Calculate the wavelength of the incident light. [2 marks]

Ooooooooooooooo — pretty patterns...

Derivation — ouch. At least it's not a bad one though. As long as you learn the diagram, it's just geometry and a bit of trig from there. Make sure you learn the equation — that way, you know what you're aiming for. As for the rest of the page, remember that the more slits you have, the sharper the image — and white light makes a pretty spectrum.

Refractive Index

The stuff on the next two pages explains why your legs look short in a swimming pool.

The **Refractive Index** of a Material Measures **How Much** It Slows Down Light

Light goes fastest in a **vacuum**. It **slows down** in other materials, because it **interacts** with the particles in them. The more **optically dense** a material is, the more light slows down when it enters it.

The **absolute refractive index** of a material, **n**, is a measure of optical density. It is found from the **ratio** between the **speed of light** in a **vacuum**, **c**, and the speed of light in that **material**, c_s.

$$n = \frac{c}{c_s}$$

$c = 3.00 \times 10^8 \text{ ms}^{-1}$

The **relative** refractive index **between two materials**, $_1n_2$, is the ratio of the speed of light **in material 1** to the speed of light **in material 2**.

$$_1n_2 = \frac{c_1}{c_2}$$

The speed of light in air is only a tiny bit smaller than c. So you can assume the refractive index of air is 1.

Combining the two equations gives:

$$_1n_2 = \frac{n_2}{n_1}$$

1) The **absolute refractive index** of a material is a **property** of that material only. A **relative refractive index** is a property of the **interface** between two materials. It's different for **every possible pair**.

2) Because you can assume $n_{air} = 1$, you can assume the refractive index for an **air to glass boundary** equals the **absolute refractive index** of the glass.

Snell's Law uses **Angles** to Calculate the Refractive Index

1) The **angle** the **incoming light** makes to the **normal** is called the **angle of incidence**, θ_1. The **angle** the **refracted ray** makes with the **normal** is the **angle of refraction**, θ_2.

2) The light is crossing a **boundary**, going from a medium with **refractive index** n_1 to a medium with refractive index n_2.

3) When light enters an **optically denser** medium it is refracted **towards** the normal.

4) **n**, θ_1 and θ_2 are related by **Snell's law**: $\boxed{n_1 \sin \theta_1 = n_2 \sin \theta_2}$

Light Leaving an **Optically Denser Material** is Refracted **Away** from the **Normal**

When light **goes from** an optically denser material into an optically **less dense** material (e.g. glass to air), interesting things can happen.

1) Shine a ray of light at a boundary going from refractive index n_1 to n_2, then gradually **increase** the angle of incidence.

2) The light is refracted away from the normal, so as you increase the angle of incidence, the angle of **refraction** gets closer and closer to **90°**.

3) Eventually θ_1 reaches a **critical angle** θ_c for which $\theta_2 = 90°$. The light is **refracted** along the **boundary**.

4) As $\sin 90° = 1$, Snell's law, $n_1 \sin \theta_1 = n_2 \sin \theta_2$, becomes $n_1 \sin \theta_c = n_2 \times 1$ so: $\boxed{\sin \theta_c = \frac{n_2}{n_1} = {}_1n_2}$

5) At θ_1 **greater** than the **critical angle**, refraction is impossible. All the light is **reflected** back into the material — this is called **total internal reflection**.

Since sin can only take values between -1 and 1, total internal reflection can only happen if $\sin \theta_c < 1$ so $_1n_2 < 1$.

Optical Fibres Use **Total Internal Reflection**

An optical fibre is a very **thin flexible tube** of **glass** or **plastic** fibre that can carry **light signals** over long distances and round corners. You only need to know about **step-index** optical fibres.

1) Step-index optical fibres themselves have a **high refractive index** but are surrounded by **cladding** with a lower refractive index to allow **total internal reflection**. Cladding also protects the fibre from **scratches** which could let **light escape**.

2) Light is shone in at **one end** of the fibre. The fibre is so **narrow** that the light always **hits the boundary** between the fibre and cladding at an **angle bigger** than the **critical angle**.

3) So all the light is **totally internally reflected** from boundary to boundary until it reaches the other end.

Refractive Index

Dispersion and Absorption Cause Signal Degradation

A **signal** (a stream of pulses of light) travelling down an optical fibre can be **degraded** by **absorption** or by **dispersion**. **Signal degradation** can cause **information** to be **lost**.

Absorption Causes Loss in Amplitude

As the signal travels, some of its energy is lost through **absorption** by the **material** the fibre is made from. This energy loss results in the **amplitude** of the signal being **reduced**.

Dispersion Causes Pulse Broadening

There are two types of dispersion that can degrade a signal.

1) **Modal dispersion** — light rays enter the fibre at different angles, and so take different **paths**. The rays which take a **longer path** take longer to reach the other end than those that travel down the **middle** of the fibre. A **single-mode** fibre only lets light take **one path**, so it stops modal dispersion.

2) **Material dispersion** — light consists of different **wavelengths** that travel at different speeds in the fibre — this causes some light wavelengths to reach the end of the fibre faster than others. Using **monochromatic light** can stop material dispersion.

Both types of dispersion lead to **pulse broadening**. The signal sent down the fibre is broader at the other end. Broadened pulses can **overlap** each other and confuse the signal.

An **optical fibre repeater** can be used to **boost** and regenerate the signal every so often, which can **reduce** signal **degradation** caused by both **absorption** and **dispersion**.

Warm-Up Questions

Q1 Why does light go fastest in a vacuum and slow down in other media?

Q2 What is the formula for the critical angle for a ray of light at a water/air boundary?

PRACTICE QUESTIONS

Exam Questions

Q1 a) Light travels in diamond at 1.24×10^8 ms^{-1}. Calculate the refractive index of diamond. [1 mark]

b) Calculate the angle of refraction if light strikes a facet of a diamond ring at an angle of 50° (to 2 s.f.) to the normal of the air/diamond boundary. [2 marks]

Q2 An adjustable underwater spotlight is placed on the floor of an aquarium tank. When the light points upwards at a steep angle a beam comes through the surface of the water into the air, and the tank is dimly lit. When the spotlight is placed at a shallower angle, no light comes up through the water surface, and the tank is brightly lit.

a) Explain what is happening. [2 marks]

b) It is found that the beam into the air disappears when the spotlight is pointed at any angle of less than 41.25° to the floor. Calculate the refractive index of water. [2 marks]

Q3 a) Explain the ways in which the cladding is designed to keep transmitted light inside an optical fibre. [2 marks]

b) The cladding functions as expected, but there is still some information loss when a step-index optical fibre is used to transmit light signals over long distances. Discuss the potential causes of this loss of information and how the design and operation of the optical fibre could be altered to reduce information loss over long transmission distances. [6 marks]

I don't care about expensive things — all I care about is wave speed...

Physics examiners are always saying how candidates do worst in the waves bit of the exam. You'd think they'd have something more important to worry about — third world poverty, war, Posh & Becks... But no.

Extra Exam Practice

To answer exam questions on <u>Section 3</u>, you need to be able to link ideas from the section together.

- Have a look at this example of how to answer a tricky exam question.
- Then check how much you've understood from Section 3 by having a go at the questions on the next page.

---

1   Read the passage below and answer the following question.

Figure 1

Human speech is caused by vibrations of the vocal cords. They produce a range of frequencies of sounds that can be varied by muscles tightening or loosening the vocal cords to alter their vibrations.

5   Tighter vocal cords produce a higher range of frequencies. The only frequencies of sound produced at the mouth are the frequencies of stationary waves in the vocal tract. These are called resonant frequencies. All other frequencies are absorbed in the vocal tract. The position of the vocal cords and the shape of the vocal tract can be altered, as shown in **Figure 1**.

10   For vowel sounds, the vocal tract can be modelled as a cylindrical tube with one open end (the mouth) and one closed end (the vocal cords), see **Figure 2**. A stationary wave in such a tube always has an antinode at the open end. The resonant

Figure 2

15   frequencies for stationary waves in such a tube are when a certain number of quarter wavelengths fit exactly in the tube. Resonant frequencies are equal to $f_n = \frac{nv}{4L}$, where v is the speed of sound in the vocal tract and n is the number of quarter wavelengths that fit into the tube, equal to a positive, odd whole number (1, 3, 5, etc). The frequency of sound determines pitch — a higher frequency sound produces a higher pitched noise.

Derive the equation for f_n on line 16. Use the equation and information from the passage to discuss the ways in which the pitch of a vowel sound can be altered by the vocal cords and vocal tract.

(6 marks)

Try using equations you know (e.g. $v = f\lambda$) that contain variables from the equation you're trying to derive.

This question can be split up into two parts, the derivation and the explanation, make sure you cover both parts to get all the marks.

1

Resonant frequencies happen when a certain number of quarter wavelengths, n, fit exactly in the tube (when n is a whole number). So $L = \frac{n\lambda}{4}$, so $\lambda = \frac{4L}{n}$. $v = f\lambda$ so $f_n = \frac{v}{\lambda} = \frac{nv}{4L}$.

Resonant frequencies can only happen with a node at one end of the tube and an antinode at the other end. This only happens when n is odd, so **n must be an odd**, whole positive number: $f_n = \frac{nv}{4L}$, $n = 1, 3, 5...$

The range of frequencies produced depends on how tight/loose the vocal cords are, so the pitch of sounds produced is limited by the vocal cords. If the vocal cords vibrate faster the pitch of sound increases. The sounds that are heard also depend on the resonant frequencies of the vocal tract. The position of the vocal cords and the vocal tract shape **changes the overall length** of the vocal tract, e.g. in Figure 1 the vocal tract is longer in the first image than the second. If L increases, the resonant frequencies, and so the pitch, will decrease as $f_n = \frac{nv}{4L}$.

You may not have studied stationary sound waves in tubes of air, but you can apply what you know about stationary waves in general to this scenario.

Don't forget you need to show why n needs to be an odd number.

Figure 1 shows that the length of the vocal tract can be changed.

Extra Exam Practice

2   Two monochromatic rays of light of different colours are incident on a surface of glass. One ray is red and one ray is blue. The glass is surrounded by transparent material cladding, as shown in **Figure 3**. Both rays are directed into the glass at the same angle to the normal, θ, and meet at the boundary between the glass and the cladding.

Figure 3

Information about the two rays of light is shown in **Table 1**.

Table 1

Colour	Frequency / $\times 10^{14}$ Hz	Refractive index of glass (n_g)	Refractive index of cladding (n_c)
Red	4.57	1.513	1.224
Blue	6.59	1.532	1.231

2.1   Use data from **Table 1** and Snell's law of refraction to determine which ray in **Figure 3** is blue light.

(3 marks)

2.2   The light rays enter the glass at an angle of $\theta = 15.0\,°$. Calculate the angle, ϕ, between the two rays of light when they meet at the boundary between the glass and the cladding.

(3 marks)

2.3   The rays reach the cladding 8.32 cm along the length of the cladding. Calculate the number of cycles that the red light goes through inside the glass before reaching the cladding.
($c = 3.00 \times 10^8$ ms^{-1})

(4 marks)

2.4   Both rays fully reflect when they meet the boundary between the glass and the cladding.
The angle θ in **Figure 3** is slowly increased for both rays of light.
Determine which ray of light will begin to refract into the cladding first as θ is increased.

(4 marks)

2.5   The rays of light are shone through a small double slit and they diffract onto a screen ahead.
The red light is shone through one slit and the blue light is shone through the other.
Explain whether you would expect to see two-source interference demonstrated on the screen.

(2 marks)

2.6   The two light ray sources are replaced with a single source that produces both rays of light in **Table 1**. The light from the source is directed at a diffraction grating perpendicular to them with a slit spacing of 2.50×10^{-6} m. Determine the highest order maxima that could be seen for each colour of light.

(1 mark)

2.7   Explain the appearance of the central maximum and the first fringe on both sides of the central maximum. You do not need to include any calculations in your answer.

(2 marks)

Scalars and Vectors

Mechanics is one of those things that you either love or hate. I won't tell you which side of the fence I'm on.

Scalars Only Have Size, but Vectors Have Size and Direction

1) A **scalar** has **no direction** — it's **just an amount** of something, like the **mass** of a **sack of meaty dog food**.

2) A **vector** has magnitude (**size**) and **direction** — like the **speed and direction** of next door's **cat** running away.

3) **Force** and **velocity** are both **vectors** — you need to know **which way** they're going as well as **how big** they are.

4) Here are a few examples to get you started:

Scalars	Vectors
mass, temperature, time, length/distance, speed, energy	displacement, velocity, force (including weight), acceleration, momentum

There are Two Methods for Adding Vectors Together

Adding two or more vectors is called finding the **resultant** of them.
There are two ways of doing this you need to know about.

Scale Drawings

Start by making a **scale drawing** of the two vectors (tip-to-tail if they're not already), draw the **resultant vector** from the tail of the first to the tip of the last, and measure its **length** and **angle**.

Example: A man walks 3.0 m on a bearing of 055° then 4.0 m east. Find the magnitude and direction (to the nearest degree) of his displacement, *s*.

The man's 'displacement' gives his position relative to his starting point.

Start by drawing a **scale diagram** for how far the man walked using a **ruler** and a **protractor**.

1 cm = 1 m drawn to scale

Then just **measure** the missing side with a ruler and the missing angle with a protractor:
s = 6.7 cm and *θ* = 75° (to the nearest degree)
So the man's displacement is **6.7 m**, on a bearing of **075°**.

Don't forget to use the scale to convert back to metres at the end.

Pythagoras and Trigonometry

When two vectors are at **right angles** to each other, you can use maths to work it out without a scale drawing.

Example: Jemima goes for a walk. She walks 3 m north and 4 m east. She has walked 7 m but she isn't 7 m from her starting point. Find the magnitude and direction (to the nearest degree) of her displacement.

First, sketch the vectors **tip-to-tail**. Then draw a line from the **tail** of the first vector to the **tip** of the last vector to give the **resultant**:
Because the vectors are at right angles, you get the **magnitude** of the resultant using Pythagoras:
$R^2 = 3^2 + 4^2 = 25$
So $R = \textbf{5 m}$

Now find the **bearing** of Jemima's new position from her original position.

You use the triangle again, but this time you need to use trigonometry. You know the opposite and the adjacent sides, so you need to use:
$\tan \theta = 4/3$
$\theta = \textbf{053°}$

Trig's really useful in mechanics — so make sure you're completely okay with it. Remember SOH CAH TOA.

Scalars and Vectors

Sometimes you have to do it backwards.

It's Useful to Split a **Vector** into **Horizontal** and **Vertical Components**

This is the opposite of finding the resultant — you start from the resultant vector and split it into two **components** at right angles to each other. You're basically **working backwards** from the examples on the other page.

Resolving a vector *v* into horizontal and vertical components

You get the **horizontal** component v_x like this:

$\cos \theta = v_x / v$

$$v_x = v \cos \theta$$

...and the **vertical** component v_y like this:

$\sin \theta = v_y / v$

$$v_y = v \sin \theta$$

In these formulae, θ is measured anticlockwise from the horizontal.

Example: Charley's amazing floating home is travelling at a speed of 5.0 ms⁻¹ at an angle of 60° (to 2 s.f.) up from the horizontal. Find the vertical and horizontal components.

The **horizontal** component v_x is:
$v_x = v \cos \theta = 5 \cos 60° = \textbf{2.5 ms}^{-1}$
The **vertical** component v_y is:
$v_y = v \sin \theta = 5 \sin 60° = \textbf{4.3 ms}^{-1}$ **(to 2 s.f.)**

Charley's mobile home was the envy of all his friends.

Resolving is dead useful because the two components of a vector **don't affect each other**. This means you can deal with the two directions **completely separately**.

Only the vertical component is affected by gravity.

Warm-Up Questions

Q1 Explain the difference between a scalar quantity and a vector quantity.

Q2 Jemima is chasing a mechanised rabbit. She follows it for 50 m in a south-east direction. It then changes direction, and she follows it a further 80 m west before catching it. By drawing a scale diagram, show that when Jemima catches the rabbit her displacement is 57 m on a bearing of 232° (to the nearest degree).

Q3 Jemima has gone for a swim in a river which is flowing at 0.35 ms⁻¹. She swims at 0.18 ms⁻¹ at right angles to the current. Show that her resultant velocity is 0.39 ms⁻¹ (to 2 s.f.) at an angle of 27° (to 2 s.f.) to the current.

Exam Questions

Q1 The wind is creating a horizontal force of 20.0 N on a falling rock of weight 75 N.
Calculate the magnitude and direction of the resultant force. [2 marks]

Q2 A glider is travelling at a velocity of 20 ms⁻¹ (to 2 s.f.) at an angle of 15° below the horizontal.
Calculate the horizontal and vertical components of the glider's velocity. [2 marks]

Mum said my life was lacking direction, so I became a vector collector...

I always think that the hardest part of vector questions is getting the initial diagram right. Once you've worked out what's going on, they're all the same — they're a piece of cake taking a walk in the park. Easy as pie in a light breeze.

Forces

Remember the vector stuff from the last two pages... good, you're going to need it...

Free-Body Force Diagrams Show All Forces on a Single Body

1) **Free-body force** diagrams show a **single body** on its own.

2) The diagram should include all the **forces** that **act on** the body, but **not** the **forces it exerts** on the rest of the world.

3) Remember **forces** are **vector quantities** and so the **arrow labels** should show the **size** and **direction** of the forces.

4) If a body is in **equilibrium** (i.e. not accelerating) the **forces** acting on it will be **balanced** in each direction.

5) A body in equilibrium can be **at rest** or moving with a **constant velocity**.

Gravity pulls satellite downwards (weight = m × g).

Gravity pulls man down. Air resistance pushes man up.

Hand pushes toy car forward. Friction pulls car backwards. Gravity pulls car down. Earth pushes car up.

All the forces in these diagrams are coplanar — they're all in the same plane. You'll only need to deal with coplanar forces.

Resolving a Force Means Splitting it into Components

1) Forces can be in **any direction**, so they're not always at right angles to each other. This is sometimes a bit **awkward** for **calculations**.

2) To make an 'awkward' force easier to deal with, you can think of it as **two separate forces**, acting at **right angles** to **each other**. Forces are **vectors**, so you can use the same method as on the previous page.

Example: The force F has exactly the same effect as the horizontal and vertical forces, F_H and F_V.
Replacing F with F_H and F_V is called **resolving** the force F.

Use these formulas when resolving forces:

$$\frac{F_H}{F} = \cos\theta \quad \text{or} \quad F_H = F\cos\theta \quad \text{and} \quad \frac{F_V}{F} = \sin\theta \quad \text{or} \quad F_V = F\sin\theta$$

Things Get Tricky with 3 Forces

1) When you have **three** coplanar forces acting on a body in **equilibrium**, you can draw the forces as a triangle, forming a **closed loop** like these:

2) Be careful when you draw the triangles not to go into autopilot and draw F_3 as the sum of F_1 and F_2 — it has to be in the **opposite** direction to balance the other two forces.

3) If it's a right-angled triangle, you can use **Pythagoras** to find a missing force.

4) If not, you might have to **resolve the forces** in each direction.

Example: 3 teams are taking part in the CGP Fun Day 3-Way Tug of War. If the knot is in equilibrium, find the size of force P.

P has no vertical component, so you can ignore the vertical components of the other teams (as they must cancel each other out). Resolve the horizontal forces (take right as the positive direction):

$(\cos 41° \times 1175) + (\cos 41° \times 1175) - P = 0$

$P = 886.7... + 886.7... = \textbf{1800 N (to 2 s.f.)}$

You can check your answer by drawing a triangle with the three forces and seeing if it forms a closed loop:

Forces

You **Add Components Back Together** to get the **Resultant Force**

1) If **two forces** act on an object, you find the **resultant** (total) **force** by adding the **vectors** together and creating a **closed triangle**, with the resultant force represented by the **third side**.

2) Forces are vectors (as you know), so you use **vector addition** — draw the forces as vector arrows put 'tip-to-tail'.

3) Then it's yet more trigonometry to find the **angle** and the **length** of the third side.

Example: Two dung beetles roll a dung ball along the ground at constant velocity. Beetle A applies a force of 0.50 N northwards while beetle B exerts a force of only 0.20 N eastwards. What is the resultant force on the dung ball?

The resultant force is **0.54 N (to 2 s.f.)** at an angle of **22° (to 2 s.f.)** from north.

By Pythagoras
$$R^2 = 0.5^2 + 0.2^2$$
$$R = \sqrt{0.29}$$
$$= 0.54 \text{ N (to 2 s.f.)}$$
$$\tan \theta = \frac{0.2}{0.5}$$
$$\theta = \tan^{-1} 0.4$$
$$\theta = 22° \text{ (to 2 s.f.)}$$

Choose Sensible **Axes** for **Resolving**

Use directions that **make sense** for the situation you're dealing with. If you've got an object on a slope, choose your directions **along the slope** and **at right angles to it**. You can turn the paper to an angle if that helps.

Always choose sensible axes

Examiners like to call a slope an "inclined plane".

The component of the bone's weight down the slope is 2.5 N so you'd need 2.5 N of friction to stop it sliding away.

Warm-Up Questions

Q1 Sketch a free-body force diagram for an ice hockey puck moving across the ice (assuming no friction).

Q2 What are the horizontal and vertical components of the force F?

PRACTICE QUESTIONS

Exam Questions

Q1 A picture with a mass of 8.0 kg is suspended from a hook as shown in the diagram. Calculate the tension force, T, in the string. Use $g = 9.81 \text{ ms}^{-2}$. [2 marks]

Q2 Two elephants pull a tree trunk as shown in the diagram. Calculate the resultant force on the tree trunk. [2 marks]

Free-body force diagram — sounds like it comes with a dance mat...

Remember those $F \cos \theta$ and $F \sin \theta$ bits. Write them on bits of paper and stick them to your wall. Scrawl them on your pillow. Tattoo them on your brain. Whatever it takes — you just have to learn them.

Moments

*This is not a time for jokes. There is not a moment to lose. Oh ho ho ho ho *bang*. (Ow.)*

A **Moment** is the **Turning Effect** of a **Force**

The **moment** of a **force** depends on the **size** of the force and **how far** the force is applied from the **turning point**:

> **moment of a force** (in Nm) = **force** (in N) × **perpendicular distance from the point to the line of action of the force** (in m)

In symbols, that's: $M = F \times d$

> The line of action of a force is a line along which it acts.

Moments Must be **Balanced** or the **Object** will **Turn**

The **principle of moments** states that for a body to be in **equilibrium**, the **sum of the clockwise moments** about any point **equals** the **sum of the anticlockwise moments** about the same point.

Example:
Two children sit on a seesaw as shown in the diagram. An adult balances the seesaw at one end. Find the size and direction of the force that the adult needs to apply.

In equilibrium, $\sum$ anticlockwise moments = $\sum$ clockwise moments

$$400 \times 1.5 = (300 \times 1) + 1.5F$$
$$600 = 300 + 1.5F$$

Final answer: $F = $ 200 N downwards

> $\sum$ means "the sum of"

Muscles, Bones and **Joints** Act as **Levers**

1) In a lever, an **effort force** (in this case from a muscle) acts against a **load force** (e.g. the weight of your arm) by means of a **rigid object** (the bone) rotating around a **pivot** (the joint).

2) You can use the **principle of moments** to answer lever questions:

Example:
Find the force, E, exerted by the biceps in holding a bag of gold still. The bag of gold weighs 100 N and the forearm weighs 20 N.

Take moments about **A.**
In equilibrium:
$$\sum \text{anticlockwise moments} = \sum \text{clockwise moments}$$
$$(100 \times 0.4) + (20 \times 0.2) = 0.04E$$
$$40 + 4 = 0.04E$$
Final answer: $E = 1100$ N

Moments

A **Couple** is a **Pair** of **Coplanar Forces**

1) A couple is a **pair** of **forces** of **equal size** which act **parallel** to each other, but in **opposite directions**. The forces are **coplanar** (see page 44).

2) A couple doesn't cause any resultant linear force, but **does** produce a **turning effect** (i.e. a moment).

The **size** of this **moment** depends on the **size** of the **forces** and the **distance** between them.

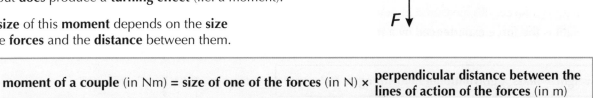

| moment of a couple (in Nm) = size of one of the forces (in N) × perpendicular distance between the lines of action of the forces (in m) |

Again, in symbols, that's: $M = F \times d$

Example:

A cyclist turns a sharp right corner by applying equal but opposite forces of 20 N to the ends of the handlebars.

The length of the handlebars is 0.6 m.
Calculate the moment applied to the handlebars.

Moment = 20 × 0.6 = **12 Nm**

Warm-Up Questions

Q1 A force of 54 N acts at a perpendicular distance of 84 cm from a pivot. Calculate the moment of the force.

Q2 A girl of mass 40 kg sits 1.5 m from the middle of a seesaw.
Show that her brother, mass 50 kg, must sit 1.2 m from the middle if the seesaw is to balance.

Q3 What is meant by the word 'couple'?

Q4 A racing car driver uses both hands to apply equal and opposite forces of 65 N to the edge of a steering wheel with radius 20 cm. Calculate the moment of the forces.

Exam Questions

Q1 A driver is changing his flat tyre. The moment required to undo the nut is 60 Nm.
He uses a 0.40 m long double-ended wheel wrench.
Calculate the force that he must apply at each end of the wrench. [2 marks]

Q2 A diver of mass 60 kg stands on the end of a diving board 2.0 m from the pivot point.
Calculate the downward force exerted on the board by the retaining spring 30 cm from the pivot.

pivot

[2 marks]

It's all about balancing — just ask a tightrope walker...

They're always boring questions aren't they — seesaws or bicycles. It'd be nice if just once, they'd have a question on... I don't know, rotating knives or something. Just something unexpected. It'd make physics a lot more fun, I'm sure.

Mass, Weight and Centre of Mass

I'm sure you know all this 'mass' and 'weight' stuff from GCSE. But let's just make sure...

The Mass of a Body makes it Resist Changes in Motion

1) The **mass** of an object is the **amount of 'stuff'** (or **matter**) in it. It's measured in **kg**.

2) The greater an object's mass, the greater its **resistance** to a **change in velocity** (called its **inertia**).

3) The **mass** of an object **doesn't change** if the strength of the **gravitational field** changes.

4) Weight is a **force**. It's measured in **newtons** (N), like all forces.

5) Weight is the **force experienced by a mass** due to a **gravitational field**.

6) The weight of an object **does vary** according to the size of the **gravitational field** acting on it.

> **weight** = **mass** × **gravitational field strength** ($W = mg$)   where g = 9.81 Nkg^{-1} on Earth.

This table shows Derek (the lion)'s mass and weight on the Earth and the Moon.

Weight 240 N

Weight 1470 N

Name	Quantity	Earth (g = 9.81 Nkg^{-1})	Moon (g = 1.6 Nkg^{-1})
Mass	Mass (scalar)	150 kg	150 kg
Weight	Force (vector)	1470 N (to 3 s.f.)	240 N (to 2 s.f.)

Centre of Mass — Assume All the Mass is in One Place

1) The **centre of mass** of an object is the **single point** that you can consider its **whole weight** to **act through** (whatever its orientation).

2) The object will always **balance** around this **point**, although in some cases the **centre of mass** will **fall outside** the object.

3) The centre of mass of a **uniform, regular solid** (e.g. a sphere, a cube) is at its **centre**.

Centre of mass

Centre of mass

Centre of mass

Find the Centre of Mass Either by Symmetry...

1) To find the centre of mass for a **regular** object you can just use **symmetry**.

2) The centre of mass of any regular shape is at its **centre** — where the lines of symmetry will cross.

3) The centre of mass is **halfway** through the **thickness** of the object at the point the lines meet.

The symmetry in this picture shows the centre of cuteness.

Centre of mass

Mass, Weight and Centre of Mass

... Or By Experiment

Experiment to find the Centre of Mass of an Irregular Object

1) **Hang** the object freely from a point (e.g. one corner).
2) Draw a **vertical line** downwards from the point of suspension — use a plumb bob to get your line exactly vertical.
3) Hang the object from a different point.
4) Draw another vertical line down.
5) The centre of mass is where the two lines **cross**.

How **Stable** an Object is Depends on its **Centre of Mass** and Base Area

1) An object will topple over if a **vertical line** drawn **downwards** from its **centre of mass** (i.e. the line of action of its weight) falls **outside** its **base area**.

2) This is because a **resultant moment** (page 46) occurs, which provides a **turning force**.

3) An object will be nice and **stable** if it has a **low centre of mass** and a **wide base area**. This idea is used a lot in design, e.g. Formula 1® racing cars.

4) The higher the centre of mass and the smaller the base area, the less stable the object is. Think of unicyclists...

No resultant moment. Bus is stable and stationary.

Net anticlockwise moment about pivot. Bus will rotate to the left and right itself.

Net clockwise moment about pivot. Bus will rotate to the right and fall over.

Warm-Up Questions

Q1 What are the differences between mass and weight?

Q2 A lioness has a mass of 200 kg. What would be her mass and weight on the Earth (where $g = 9.81$ Nkg⁻¹) and on the Moon (where $g = 1.6$ Nkg⁻¹)?

Q3 What is meant by the centre of mass of an object?

Q4 Why will an object topple if its centre of mass is not over the object's base?

Exam Question

Q1 a) Describe an experiment to find the centre of mass of an object of uniform density with a constant thickness and irregular cross-section. Identify one major source of uncertainty and suggest a way to reduce its effect on your result. [5 marks]

b) Explain why you would not need to conduct this experiment for a regular, uniform solid. [1 mark]

The centre of mass of this book should be round about page 62...

This is a really useful area of physics. To would-be nuclear physicists it might seem a little dull, but if you want to be an engineer — something a bit more useful (no offence Einstein) — then things like centre of mass are dead important things to understand. You know, for designing things like cars and submarines... yep, pretty useful I'd say.

Displacement-Time Graphs

Drawing graphs by hand — oh joy. You'd think examiners had never heard of the graphical calculator.
Ah well, until they manage to drag themselves out of the dark ages, you'll just have to grit your teeth and get on with it.

Displacement, Velocity, and Acceleration are All Linked

Displacement, velocity and acceleration are all **vector** quantities (page 42), so the direction matters.

> **Speed** — How fast something is moving, regardless of direction.
> **Displacement** (s) — How far an object's travelled from its starting point in a given direction.
> **Velocity** (v) — The rate of change of an object's displacement (its speed in a given direction).
> **Acceleration** (a) — The rate of change of an object's velocity.

You need to know these formulas for **velocity** and **acceleration**:

$$v = \frac{\Delta s}{\Delta t} \quad \text{and} \quad a = \frac{\Delta v}{\Delta t}$$

The triangle symbol is the Greek 'delta', and it means 'the change in'.

The speed (or velocity) of an object at any given point in time is known as its **instantaneous** speed (or velocity).
To find the **average** speed (or velocity), divide the **total** distance or displacement by the total time.

Acceleration Means a Curved Displacement-Time Graph

A graph of displacement against time for an **accelerating object** always produces a **curve**.
If the object is accelerating at a **uniform rate**, then the **rate of change** of the **gradient** will be constant.

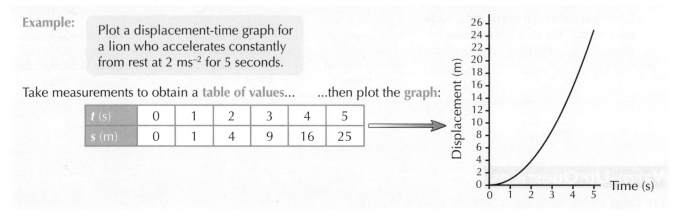

Example:

Plot a displacement-time graph for a lion who accelerates constantly from rest at 2 ms⁻² for 5 seconds.

Take measurements to obtain a table of values... ...then plot the graph:

t (s)	0	1	2	3	4	5
s (m)	0	1	4	9	16	25

Different Accelerations Have Different Gradients

In the example above, if the lion has a **different acceleration** it'll change the **gradient** of the curve like this:

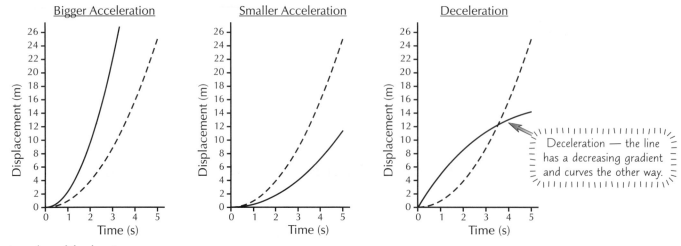

Bigger Acceleration

Smaller Acceleration

Deceleration

Deceleration — the line has a decreasing gradient and curves the other way.

Displacement-Time Graphs

The **Gradient** of a **Displacement-Time Graph** Tells You the Velocity

When the velocity is constant, the graph's a **straight line**.
As you saw on the previous page, velocity is defined as...

$$\text{velocity} = \frac{\text{change in displacement}}{\text{change in time}}$$

On the graph, this is $\frac{\text{change in } y \ (\Delta y)}{\text{change in } x \ (\Delta x)}$, i.e. the gradient.

So to get the velocity from a displacement-time graph,
just find the gradient.

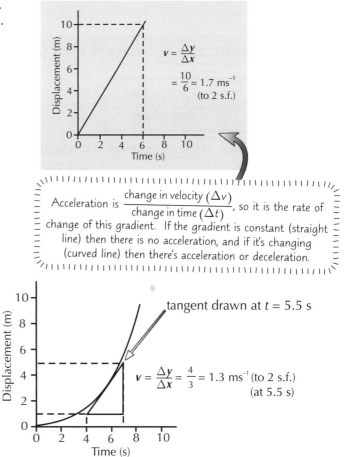

$v = \frac{\Delta y}{\Delta x}$

$= \frac{10}{6} = 1.7 \ ms^{-1}$ (to 2 s.f.)

Acceleration is $\frac{\text{change in velocity } (\Delta v)}{\text{change in time } (\Delta t)}$, so it is the rate of change of this gradient. If the gradient is constant (straight line) then there is no acceleration, and if it's changing (curved line) then there's acceleration or deceleration.

It's the Same with **Curved Graphs**

If the gradient **isn't constant** (i.e. if it's a curved line),
it means the object is **accelerating**.

> To find the **instantaneous velocity** at a certain
> point you need to draw a **tangent** to the curve
> at that point and find its gradient.

To find the **average velocity** over a period of time,
just divide the total change in displacement by
the total change in time — it doesn't matter if the
graph is curved or not.

tangent drawn at $t = 5.5$ s

$v = \frac{\Delta y}{\Delta x} = \frac{4}{3} = 1.3 \ ms^{-1}$ (to 2 s.f.)
(at 5.5 s)

Warm-Up Questions

Q1 What is given by the slope of a displacement-time graph?

Q2 Sketch a displacement-time graph to show: a) constant velocity, b) acceleration, c) deceleration

PRACTICE QUESTIONS

Exam Questions

Q1 Describe the motion of the cyclist as shown by the graph below. [4 marks]

Q2 A baby crawls 5 m in 8 seconds at a constant velocity. She then rests for 5 seconds before
crawling a further 3 m in 5 seconds. Finally, she makes her way back to her starting point in
10 seconds, travelling at a constant speed all the way.

a) Draw a displacement-time graph to show the baby's journey. [4 marks]

b) Calculate her average velocity at all the different stages of her journey. [2 marks]

Some curves are bigger than others...

*Whether it's a straight line or a curve, the steeper it is, the greater the velocity. There's nothing difficult about these
graphs — the problem is that it's easy to get them muddled up with velocity-time graphs (next page). Just think about
the gradient — is it velocity or acceleration, is it changing (curve) or constant (straight line), is it 0 (horizontal line)...*

Velocity-Time and Acceleration-Time Graphs

Speed-time graphs and velocity-time graphs are pretty similar. The big difference is that velocity-time graphs can have a negative part to show something travelling in the opposite direction:

The **Gradient** of a **Velocity-Time Graph** Tells You the **Acceleration**

$$\text{acceleration} = \frac{\text{change in velocity}}{\text{time taken}}$$

likewise for a speed-time graph

So the acceleration is just the **gradient** of a **velocity-time graph**.

1) **Uniform** acceleration is always a **straight line**.
   The **steeper** the **gradient**, the **greater** the **acceleration**.

2) A **curved** graph shows **changing** acceleration. **Increasing** gradient means **increasing acceleration**, and **decreasing** gradient means **decreasing acceleration** (or deceleration).

Example: A lion strolls along at 1.5 ms⁻¹ for 4 s and then accelerates uniformly at a rate of 2.5 ms⁻² for 4 s. Plot this information on a velocity-time graph.

So, for the first four seconds, the velocity is 1.5 ms⁻¹, then it increases by **2.5 ms⁻¹** every second:

t (s)	v (ms⁻¹)
0 – 4	1.5
5	4.0
6	6.5
7	9.0
8	11.5

Norman (the lion*)...

$$a = \frac{\Delta v}{\Delta t} = \frac{11.5 - 1.5}{4} = 2.5 \text{ ms}^{-2}$$

You can see that the **gradient of the line** is **constant** between 4 s and 8 s and has a value of 2.5 ms⁻², representing the **acceleration of the lion**.

Yes, I know — I just like lions, OK...

Displacement = Area Under Velocity-Time Graph

You know that: **distance travelled = average speed × time**

The **area under a velocity-time graph** tells you the displacement of the object. The magnitude of this displacement is the distance that object has travelled.

You can calculate areas using geometry or counting grid squares and multiplying the number by the value of each square.

Example: A ball is dropped from table-height so it bounces vertically. It bounces twice before someone catches it. The ball's motion while it bounces is shown on the *v-t* graph below. Calculate how high the ball rebounds on the first bounce.

Before you try and calculate anything, make sure you understand what each part of the graph is telling you about the ball's motion.

1) When the ball is first dropped, the velocity of the ball is **negative** — so downwards is the negative direction.

2) The points where the **ball hits the floor** are shown by the **vertical straight lines** on the graph — the ball's **speed** remains roughly the **same**, but its **direction** (and **velocity**) changes the instant it hits the floor.

3) The points where the ball's velocity is **zero** show where the ball reaches the **top of a bounce** before starting to fall downwards.

The height of the first bounce is the **area under the graph** between the time the ball first rebounds from the floor and the time it reaches the top of the bounce.

displacement = area under graph
$= (3.5 \times 0.35) \div 2 = 0.6125 = \textbf{0.61 m (to 2 s.f.)}$

Velocity-Time and Acceleration-Time Graphs

Acceleration-Time Graphs are Useful Too

An **acceleration-time** (*a/t*) graph shows how an object's **acceleration** changes over time.

1) The **height** of the graph gives the object's **acceleration** at that time.
2) The **area** under the graph gives the object's **change in velocity**.
3) If $a = 0$, then the object is moving with **constant velocity**.
4) A negative acceleration is a **deceleration**.

Example: The acceleration of a car in a drag race is shown in this acceleration-time graph.

a) **After how many seconds does the car reach its maximum velocity?**
When the acceleration is 0, i.e. after **4 seconds**.

b) **If the car was stationary at *t* = 0 s, calculate its maximum velocity.**
(Change in) velocity = area under graph
$$= 0.5 \times 4 \times 25 = \mathbf{50\ ms^{-1}}$$

You Can Draw Displacement-Time and Velocity-Time Graphs Using ICT

Instead of gathering distance and time data using **traditional methods**, e.g. a stopwatch and ruler, you can be a bit more **high-tech**.

A fairly **standard** piece of kit you can use for motion experiments is an **ultrasound position detector**. This is a type of **data-logger** that automatically records the **distance** of an object from the sensor several times a second.

If you attach one of these detectors to a computer with **graph-drawing software**, you can get **real-time** displacement-time and velocity-time graphs.

> The main advantages of data-loggers over traditional methods are:
>
> 1) The data is more accurate — you don't have to allow for human reaction times.
>
> 2) Automatic systems have a much higher sampling rate than humans — most ultrasound position detectors can take a reading ten times every second.
>
> 3) You can see the data displayed in real time.

Warm-Up Questions

Q1 How do you calculate acceleration from a velocity-time graph?
Q2 How do you calculate the displacement travelled from a velocity-time graph?
Q3 Sketch velocity-time graphs for constant velocity and constant acceleration.
Q4 Sketch velocity-time and acceleration-time graphs for a boy bouncing on a trampoline.
Q5 What does the area under an acceleration-time graph tell you?
Q6 Describe the main advantages of ICT over traditional methods for the collection and display of motion data.

Exam Question

Q1 A skier accelerates uniformly from rest at 2 ms^{-2} down a straight slope for 5 seconds. He then reaches the bottom of the slope and continues along the flat ground, decelerating at 1 ms^{-2} until he stops.

a) Sketch the velocity-time and acceleration-time graphs for his journey. [4 marks]

b) Use your *v-t* graph from part a) to find the distance travelled by the skier during the first 5 seconds. [2 marks]

Still awake — I'll give you five more minutes...

There's a really nice sunset outside my window. It's one of those ones that makes the whole landscape go pinky-yellowish. And that's about as much interest as I can muster on this topic. Normal service will be resumed on page 54.

Motion With Uniform Acceleration

Uniform Acceleration is Constant Acceleration

Acceleration could mean a change in speed or direction or both.

Uniform means **constant** here. It's nothing to do with what you wear.
There are **four main equations** that you use to solve problems involving **uniform acceleration**. You need to be able to **use them**, but you don't have to know how they're **derived** — we've just put it in to help you learn them.

1) **Acceleration is the rate of change of velocity.**
From this definition you get:

$$a = \frac{(v - u)}{t} \quad \text{so} \quad \boxed{v = u + at}$$

where:
u = initial velocity a = acceleration
v = final velocity t = time taken

2) **s = average velocity × time**
If acceleration is constant, the average velocity is just the average of the initial and final velocities, so:

$$\boxed{s = \frac{(u + v)}{2} \times t} \quad s = \text{displacement}$$

3) Substitute the expression for v from equation 1 into equation 2 to give:

$$s = \frac{(u + u + at) \times t}{2} = \frac{2ut + at^2}{2} \quad \boxed{s = ut + \tfrac{1}{2}at^2}$$

4) You can **derive** the fourth equation from equations **1** and **2**:

Use equation **1** in the form:
$$a = \frac{(v - u)}{t}$$

Multiply both sides by s, where:
$$s = \frac{(u + v)}{2} \times t$$

This gives us:
$$as = \frac{(v - u)}{t} \times \frac{(u + v)t}{2}$$

The t's on the right cancel, so:
$$2as = (v - u)(v + u)$$
$$2as = v^2 - uv + uv - u^2$$

so: $$\boxed{v^2 = u^2 + 2as}$$

Example: A tile falls from a roof 25 m high. Calculate its speed when it hits the ground and how long it takes to fall. Take $g = 9.81$ ms^{-2}.

First of all, write out what you know:
$s = 25$ m
$u = 0$ ms^{-1} since the tile's stationary to start with
$a = 9.81$ ms^{-2} due to gravity
$v = ?$ $t = ?$

Usually you take upwards as the positive direction. In this question it's probably easier to take downwards as positive, so you get $g = +9.81$ ms^{-2} instead of $g = -9.81$ ms^{-2}.

9.81 ms^{-2}

25 m

Then, choose an equation with only **one unknown quantity**.
So start with $v^2 = u^2 + 2as$
$v^2 = 0 + 2 \times 9.81 \times 25$
$v^2 = 490.5$
$v = 22$ ms^{-1} (to 2 s.f.)

Now, find t using:
$s = ut + \tfrac{1}{2}at^2$
$25 = 0 + \tfrac{1}{2} \times 9.81 \times t^2$
$t^2 = \frac{25}{4.9}$
$t = 2.3$ (to 2 s.f.)

Final answers:
$t = 2.3$ s (to 2 s.f.)
$v = 22$ ms^{-1} (to 2 s.f.)

Motion With Uniform Acceleration

Example: A car accelerates steadily from rest at a rate of 4.2 ms^{-2} for 6.5 seconds.
a) Calculate the final speed.
b) Calculate the distance travelled in 6.5 seconds.

4.2 ms^{-2}

Remember — always start by writing down what you know.

a) $a = 4.2$ ms^{-2} choose the right equation… $v = u + at$
$u = 0$ ms^{-1} $v = 0 + 4.2 \times 6.5$
$t = 6.5$ s   **Final answer:** $v = 27.3$ ms^{-1}
$v = ?$ $= \textbf{27 ms}^{-1}$ **(to 2 s.f.)**

b) $s = ?$ you can use: $s = \dfrac{(u + v)t}{2}$ or: $s = ut + \frac{1}{2}at^2$
$t = 6.5$ s
$u = 0$ ms^{-1}
$a = 4.2$ ms^{-2} $s = \dfrac{(0 + 27.3) \times 6.5}{2}$ $s = 0 + \frac{1}{2} \times 4.2 \times (6.5)^2$
$v = 27.3$ ms^{-1}

                     Final answer: $s = \textbf{89 m}$ **(to 2 s.f.)** $s = \textbf{89 m}$ **(to 2 s.f.)**

Warm-Up Questions

Q1 Write out the four uniform acceleration equations.

Q2 A small steel ball is dropped from a height of 1.5 m. Calculate its speed as it hits the ground.

PRACTICE QUESTIONS

Exam Questions

Q1 A skydiver jumps from a helicopter hovering at a height of 1500 m from the ground.
She accelerates due to gravity for 5.0 s.
a) Calculate her maximum vertical velocity. (Assume no air resistance.) [2 marks]

b) Calculate how far she falls in this time. [2 marks]

Q2 A motorcyclist slows down uniformly as he approaches a red light.
He takes 3.2 seconds to come to a halt and travels 40 m (to 2 s.f.) in this time.
a) Calculate how fast he was initially travelling. [2 marks]

b) Calculate his acceleration. (N.B. a negative value shows a deceleration.) [2 marks]

Q3 A stream provides a constant acceleration of 6 ms^{-2}. A toy boat is pushed directly against the current
and then released from a point 1.2 m upstream from a small waterfall. Just before it reaches the waterfall,
it is travelling at a speed of 5 ms^{-1}.
a) Calculate the initial velocity of the boat. [2 marks]

b) Calculate the maximum distance upstream from the waterfall the boat reaches. [2 marks]

Constant acceleration — it'll end in tears...

If a question talks about "uniform" or "constant" acceleration, it's a dead giveaway they want you to use one of these equations. The tricky bit is working out which one to use — start every question by writing out what you know and what you need to know. That makes it much easier to see which equation you need. To be sure. Arrr.

Acceleration Due to Gravity

Ahhh acceleration due to gravity. The reason falling apples whack you on the head.

Free Fall is When There's Only Gravity and Nothing Else

Free fall is defined as the motion of an object undergoing an acceleration of 'g'. You need to remember:
1) Acceleration is a **vector quantity** — and 'g' acts **vertically downwards**.
2) The magnitude of 'g' is usually taken as **9.81 ms⁻²**, though it varies slightly at different points on the Earth's surface.
3) The **only force** acting on an object in free fall is its **weight**.
4) Objects can have an initial velocity in any direction and still undergo **free fall** as long as the **force** providing the initial velocity is **no longer acting**.

All Objects in Free Fall Accelerate at the Same Rate

1) For over 1000 years the generally accepted theory was that heavier objects would fall towards the ground quicker than lighter objects. It was challenged a few times, but it was finally overturned when **Galileo** came on the scene.
2) The difference with Galileo was that he set up **systematic** and **rigorous experiments** to **test** his theories — just like in modern science. These experiments could be repeated and the results described **mathematically** and compared.

Another gravity experiment.

3) Galileo believed that all objects fall at the same rate. The problem in trying to prove it was that free-falling objects **fell too quickly** for him to be able to take any accurate measurements (he only had a water clock), and **air resistance** affects the rate at which objects fall.
4) Galileo measured the time a ball took to roll down a **smooth** groove in an inclined plane. He killed two birds with one stone by rolling it down a plane, which **slows** the ball's fall as well as reducing the effect of **air resistance**.
5) By rolling the ball along different fractions of the total length of the slope, he found that the distance the ball travelled was proportional to the square of the time taken. The ball was **accelerating** at a **constant rate**.

ball at rest at the top of the slope

smooth surface

accelerating ball

6) In the end it took **Newton** to bring it all together to show and explain why **all** free falling objects have the same acceleration. He showed **mathematically** that all objects are attracted towards the Earth due to a force he called **gravity**. Ah, good ol' Newton...

You Can Calculate *g* By Performing an Experiment...

PRACTICAL SKILLS

This is just one way of **measuring** g, there are loads of different experiments you could do — just make sure you know **one** method for your exams.

1) Set up the equipment shown in the diagram on the right.
2) Measure the height *h* from the **bottom** of the ball bearing to the **trapdoor**.
3) Flick the switch to simultaneously **start the timer** and **disconnect the electromagnet**, releasing the ball bearing.
4) The ball bearing falls, knocking the trapdoor down and **breaking the circuit** — which **stops the timer**. Record the time *t* shown on the timer.
5) **Repeat** this experiment three times and **average** the time taken to fall from this height. Repeat this experiment but drop the ball from several **different heights**.
6) You can then use these results to find *g* using a **graph** (see the next page).

electromagnet

ball bearing

switch

timer

height *h*

trapdoor

- Using a **small** and **heavy** ball bearing means you can assume air resistance is so small you can **ignore it**.
- Having a computer **automatically release** and **time** the ball-bearing's fall can measure times with a **smaller uncertainty** than if you tried to drop the ball and time the fall using a stopwatch.
- The most significant source of **error** in this experiment will be in the measurement of *h*. Using a ruler, you'll have an uncertainty of about ±1 mm. This dwarfs any error from switch delay or air resistance.

Acceleration Due to Gravity

PRACTICAL SKILLS

1) Use your data from the experiment on the last page to plot a graph of **height** (s) against the **time** it takes the ball to fall, **squared** (t^2). Then draw a **line of best fit**.

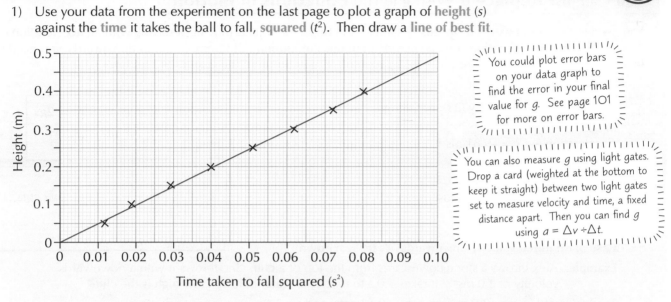

You could plot error bars on your data graph to find the error in your final value for g. See page 101 for more on error bars.

You can also measure g using light gates. Drop a card (weighted at the bottom to keep it straight) between two light gates set to measure velocity and time, a fixed distance apart. Then you can find g using $a = \Delta v \div \Delta t$.

2) You know that with constant acceleration, $s = ut + \frac{1}{2}at^2$. If you drop the ball, initial speed $u = 0$, so $s = \frac{1}{2}at^2$.

3) Rearranging this gives $\frac{1}{2}a = \frac{s}{t^2}$, or $\frac{1}{2}g = \frac{s}{t^2}$ (remember the acceleration is all due to gravity).

4) So the gradient of the line of best fit, $\frac{\Delta s}{\Delta t^2}$, is equal to $\frac{1}{2}g$: $\quad g = 2 \times \frac{\Delta s}{\Delta t^2} = 2 \times \frac{0.44}{0.09} = 9.8\ \text{ms}^{-2}$ (to 2 s.f.)

In the exam you might be asked to find g from a displacement-time graph (see page 51). g is an acceleration and the gradient of the graph will be velocity, so you can find g by finding the change in gradient between two points on the graph (as $a = \Delta v \div \Delta t$).

Warm-Up Questions

Q1 What is meant by free fall?

Q2 How does the velocity of a free-falling object change with time?

Q3 What is the main reason Galileo's ideas became generally accepted in place of the old theory?

Q4 Describe an experiment that could be used to calculate the value of g.

PRACTICE QUESTIONS

Exam Question

Q1 In an experiment to determine the value of g, a small steel ball is dropped from a range of heights. The time it takes to reach the ground when dropped from each height is recorded.

a) Explain why using a steel ball is better than using a beach ball in this experiment. [1 mark]

b) State one random error that could arise from this experiment and suggest a way to remove it. [2 marks]

c) State one systematic error that could arise from this experiment and suggest a way to remove it. [2 marks]

d) A graph of the distance travelled by the ball against time taken squared is plotted. Show that the gradient of the graph is equal to half the value of g. [3 marks]

So it's this "Galileo" geezer who's to blame for my practicals...

Hmmm... I wonder what Galileo would be proudest of — insisting on the systematic, rigorous experimental method on which modern science hangs... or getting in a Queen song? Magnificoooooo...

Projectile Motion

Calculators at the ready — it's time to resolve more things into vertical and horizontal components.
It can be a bit tricky at first, but you'll soon get the hang of it. Chop chop, no time to lose.

You Can Just **Replace** a With g in the **Equations of Motion**

You need to be able to work out **speeds**, **distances** and **times** for objects moving vertically with an **acceleration** of g. As g is a **constant acceleration** you can use the **equations of motion**. But because g acts downwards, you need to be careful about directions, here we've taken **upwards as positive** and **downwards as negative**.

Case 1: No initial velocity (it's just falling)

Initial velocity $u = 0$
Acceleration $a = g = -9.81$ ms^{-2}. Hence the equations of motion become:

$$v = gt \qquad v^2 = 2gs$$
$$s = \tfrac{1}{2}gt^2 \qquad s = \frac{vt}{2}$$

Case 2: An initial velocity upwards (it's thrown up into the air)

The equations of motion are just as normal,
but with $a = g = -9.81$ ms^{-2}.

Sign Conventions — Learn Them:
g is always <u>downwards</u> so it's <u>usually negative</u>
t is <u>always positive</u>
u and v can be either <u>positive</u> or <u>negative</u>
s can be either <u>positive</u> or <u>negative</u>

Case 3: An initial velocity downwards (it's thrown down)

Example: Alex throws a stone downwards from the top of a cliff. She throws it with a downwards velocity of 2.0 ms^{-1}. It takes 3.0 s to reach the water below. How high is the cliff?

1) You know $u = -2.0$ ms^{-1}, $a = g = -9.81$ ms^{-2} and $t = 3.0$ s. You need to find s.

2) Use $s = ut + \tfrac{1}{2}gt^2 = (-2.0 \times 3.0) + \left(\tfrac{1}{2} \times -9.81 \times 3.0^2\right) = -50.145$ m. The cliff is **50 m (to 2 s.f.)** high.

s is negative because the stone ends up further down than it
started. Height is a scalar quantity, so is always positive.

You Have to Think of **Horizontal** and **Vertical** Motion **Separately**

Example: Sharon fires a scale model of a TV talent show presenter horizontally with a velocity of 100 ms^{-1} (to 3 s.f.) from 1.5 m above the ground. How long does it take to hit the ground, and how far does it travel horizontally? Assume the model acts as a particle, the ground is horizontal and there is no air resistance.

Think about the vertical motion first:

1) It's **constant acceleration** under gravity...

2) You know $u = 0$ (no vertical velocity at first), $s = -1.5$ m and $a = g = -9.81$ ms^{-2}. You need to find t.

3) Use $s = \tfrac{1}{2}gt^2 \Rightarrow t = \sqrt{\dfrac{2s}{g}} = \sqrt{\dfrac{2 \times -1.5}{-9.81}} = 0.55300...$ s

4) So the model hits the ground after **0.55 seconds (to 2 s.f.)**.

Then do the horizontal motion:

1) The horizontal motion isn't affected by gravity or any other force, so it moves at a **constant speed**.

2) That means you can just use good old **speed = distance / time**.

3) Now $v_H = 100$ ms^{-1}, $t = 0.55300...$ s and $a = 0$. You need to find s_H.

4) $s_H = v_H t = 100 \times 0.55300... = $ **55 m (to 2 s.f.)**

Where v_H is the horizontal velocity, and
s_H is the horizontal distance travelled
(rather than the height fallen).

Projectile Motion

It's **Slightly Trickier** if it **Starts Off** at an **Angle**

If something's projected at an angle (like, say, a javelin) you start off with both horizontal and vertical velocity:

Method:
1) Resolve the initial velocity into horizontal and vertical components.
2) Use the vertical component to work out how long it's in the air and/or how high it goes.
3) Use the horizontal component to work out how far it goes horizontally while it's in the air.

Example: A cannonball is fired from ground height at an angle of exactly 40° with an initial velocity of 15 ms⁻¹. Calculate how far the cannonball travels before it hits the ground. Assume no air resistance.

Resolve the velocity into horizontal and vertical components:

Horizontal component $u_H = \cos 40° \times 15 = 11.49...$ ms⁻¹
Vertical component $u_V = \sin 40° \times 15 = 9.64...$ ms⁻¹

Use the vertical component to work out how long the cannonball is in the air:

1) Halfway through the ball's flight, its v_v will be zero. $u_V = 9.64...$ ms⁻¹, $a = -9.81$ ms⁻², $t = ?$,

Use $v_V = u_V + at$: $0 = 9.64... + (-9.81 \times t) \Rightarrow t = \dfrac{9.64...}{9.81} = 0.98...$ s

2) So the time it takes to reach the ground again = $2 \times 0.98... = 1.96...$ s

Use the horizontal component to work out how far it goes while it's in the air:

There's no horizontal acceleration, so $u_H = v_H = 11.49...$ ms⁻¹.
Distance = constant speed × time = $11.49... \times 1.96... = 22.58... = $ **23 m (to 2 s.f.)**

Warm-Up Questions

Q1 What is the initial vertical velocity for an object projected horizontally with a velocity of 5 ms⁻¹?

Q2 What is the initial horizontal velocity of an object projected at 45 degrees to the ground with a velocity of 25 ms⁻¹?

Exam Questions

Q1 Jason stands on a vertical cliff edge throwing stones into the sea below.
He throws a stone horizontally with a velocity of exactly 20 ms⁻¹, 560 m above sea level.

a) Calculate the time taken for the stone to hit the water from leaving Jason's hand.
Use $g = 9.81$ ms⁻² and ignore air resistance. [2 marks]

b) Calculate the distance of the stone from the base of the cliff when it hits the water. [2 marks]

Q2 Robin fires an arrow into the air with a vertical velocity of exactly 30 ms⁻¹, and a horizontal velocity of exactly 20 ms⁻¹, from 1 m above the ground. Calculate the maximum height from the ground reached by his arrow to the nearest metre. Use $g = 9.81$ ms⁻² and ignore air resistance. [3 marks]

All this physics makes me want to create projectile motions...

...by throwing my revision books out of the window. The maths on this page can be tricky, but take it step by step and all will be fine. Plus, the next page is all about Newton, and I must say he was a mighty clever chap.

Newton's Laws of Motion

You did most of this at GCSE, but that doesn't mean you can just skip over it now. You'll be kicking yourself if you forget this stuff in the exam — it's easy marks...

Newton's **1st Law** Says That a **Force** is Needed to Change Velocity

1) **Newton's 1st law of motion** states that the **velocity** of an object will **not change** unless a **resultant force** acts on it.

2) In plain English this means a body will stay still or move in a **straight line** at a **constant speed**, unless there's a **resultant force** acting on it.

An apple sitting on a table won't go anywhere because the forces on it are balanced.

| reaction (*R*) | = | weight (*mg*) |
| (force of table pushing apple up) | | (force of gravity pulling apple down) |

3) If the forces **aren't balanced**, the **overall resultant force** will make the body **accelerate**. This could be a change in **direction**, or **speed**, or both. (See Newton's 2nd law, below.)

Newton's **2nd Law** Says That **Acceleration** is **Proportional** to the Force

...which can be written as the well-known equation:

resultant force (N) = mass (kg) × acceleration (ms^{-2})

$$F = m \times a$$

Learn this — it crops up all over the place in Physics. And learn what it means too:

1) It says that the **more force** you have acting on a certain mass, the **more acceleration** you get.

2) It says that for a given force the **more mass** you have, the **less acceleration** you get.

3) There's more on this most excellent law on p.65.

REMEMBER:
1) The **resultant force** is the **vector sum** of all the forces.
2) The force is **always** measured in **newtons**.
3) The **mass** is always measured in **kilograms**.
4) The **acceleration** is always in the **same direction** as the **resultant force** and is measured in **ms^{-2}**.

Galileo said: **All Objects Fall** at the **Same Rate** (if You **Ignore Air Resistance**)

You need to understand **why** this is true. Newton's 2nd law explains it neatly — consider two balls dropped at the same time — ball **1** being heavy, and ball **2** being light. Then use Newton's 2nd law to find their acceleration.

mass = m_1
resultant force = F_1
acceleration = a_1
By Newton's Second Law:
$$F_1 = m_1 a_1$$
Ignoring air resistance, the only force acting on the ball is weight, given by $W_1 = m_1 g$ (where g = gravitational field strength = 9.81 Nkg^{-1}).
So: $F_1 = m_1 a_1 = W_1 = m_1 g$
So: $m_1 a_1 = m_1 g$, then m_1 cancels out to give: $a_1 = g$

mass = m_2
resultant force = F_2
acceleration = a_2
By Newton's Second Law:
$$F_2 = m_2 a_2$$
Ignoring air resistance, the only force acting on the ball is weight, given by $W_2 = m_2 g$ (where g = gravitational field strength = 9.81 Nkg^{-1}).
So: $F_2 = m_2 a_2 = W_2 = m_2 g$
So: $m_2 a_2 = m_2 g$, then m_2 cancels out to give: $a_2 = g$

...in other words, the **acceleration** is **independent of the mass**. It makes **no difference** whether the ball is **heavy or light**. And I've kindly **hammered home the point** by showing you two almost identical examples.

Newton's Laws of Motion

Newton's **3rd Law** Says Each Force has an **Equal, Opposite Reaction Force**

There are a few different ways of stating Newton's 3rd law, but the clearest way is:

> **If an object A EXERTS a FORCE on object B, then object B exerts AN EQUAL BUT OPPOSITE FORCE on object A.**

You'll also hear the law as "every action has an equal and opposite reaction". But this confuses people who wrongly think the forces are both applied to the same object. (If that were the case, you'd get a resultant force of zero and nothing would ever move anywhere...)

The two forces actually represent the **same interaction**, just seen from two **different perspectives**:

1) If you **push against a wall**, the wall will **push back** against you, **just as hard**. As soon as you stop pushing, so does the wall. Amazing...

2) If you **pull a cart**, whatever force **you exert** on the rope, the rope exerts the **exact opposite** pull on you (unless the rope's stretching).

3) When you go **swimming**, you push **back** against the water with your arms and legs, and the water pushes you **forwards** with an equal-sized force.

This looks like Newton's 3rd law...

But it's <u>NOT</u>.

Newton's 3rd law applies in **all situations** and to all **types of force**. But the pairs of forces are always the **same type**, e.g. both gravitational or both electrical.

...because both forces are acting on the book, and they're not of the same type. They are two separate interactions. The forces are equal and opposite, resulting in zero acceleration, so this is showing Newton's 1st law.

Warm-Up Questions

Q1 State Newton's 1st, 2nd and 3rd laws of motion, and explain what they mean.

Q2 What are the two equal and opposite forces acting between an orbiting satellite and the Earth?

Exam Questions

Q1 A boat is moving across a river. The engines provide a force of 500 N at right angles to the flow of the river and the boat experiences a drag of 100 N in the opposite direction. The force on the boat due to the flow of the river is 300 N. The mass of the boat is 250 kg.

a) Calculate the magnitude of the resultant force acting on the boat. [2 marks]

b) Calculate the magnitude of the acceleration of the boat. [2 marks]

Q2 John's bike, which has a mass of m, breaks and he has to push it home. The bike has a constant acceleration a and a frictional force F opposes the motion. What force is John is using to push his bike?

A	ma
B	$ma + F$
C	$m(a - F)$
D	$ma - F$

[1 mark]

Q3 Michael and Tom are both keen on diving. They notice that they seem to take the same time to drop from the diving board to the water. Use Newton's second law to explain why this is the case. (Assume no air resistance.) [3 marks]

Newton's three incredibly important laws of motion...

These laws may not really fill you with a huge amount of excitement (and I could hardly blame you if they don't)... but it was pretty fantastic at the time — suddenly people actually understood how forces work, and how they affect motion. I mean arguably it was one of the most important scientific discoveries ever...

Drag, Lift and Terminal Speed

If you jump out of a plane at 1500 m, you want to know that you're not going to be accelerating all the way.

Friction is a Force that Opposes Motion

There are two main types of friction — **dry friction** between **solid surfaces** and **fluid friction** (known as **drag**, fluid resistance or air resistance).

Fluid Friction or Drag:

1) 'Fluid' is a word that means either a **liquid or a gas** — something that can **flow**.

2) The force depends on the thickness (or **viscosity**) of the fluid.

3) It **increases** as the **speed increases** (for simple situations it's directly proportional, but you don't need to worry about the mathematical relationship).

4) It also depends on the **shape** of the object moving through it — the larger the **area** pushing against the fluid, the greater the resistance force.

5) A **projectile** (see p. 58) is **slowed down** by air resistance. If you calculate how far a projectile will travel without thinking about air resistance, your answer will be **too large**.

Things you need to remember about frictional forces:

1) They **always** act in the **opposite direction** to the **motion** of the object.

2) They can **never** speed things up or start something moving.

3) They convert **kinetic energy** into **heat** and **sound**.

Lift is Perpendicular to Fluid Flow

1) '**Lift**' is an **upwards force** on an object moving through a fluid.

2) It happens when the shape of an object causes the fluid flowing over it to **change direction**.

3) The force acts **perpendicular** to the direction the fluid flows in.

Example: Cross-section of a plane wing moving through air

As the wing moves through the air, it pushes down on the air (and changes its direction).

This causes an equal and opposite reaction force on the wing (Newton's third law, see p.61).

drag
force of the wing on the air flow
lift

Terminal Speed — When the Friction Force Equals the Driving Force

You will reach a **terminal (maximum) speed** at some point, if you have:

1) a **driving force** that stays the **same** all the time

2) a **frictional** or **drag force** (or collection of forces) that increases with speed

There are **three main stages** to reaching terminal speed:

The car accelerates from rest using a constant driving force.

As the speed increases, the frictional forces increase (because of things like turbulence — you don't need the details). This reduces the resultant force on the car and hence reduces its acceleration.

Eventually the car reaches a speed at which the frictional forces are equal to the driving force. There is now no resultant force and no acceleration, so the car carries on at constant speed.

Different factors affect a vehicle's maximum speed

As you just saw, a vehicle reaches maximum speed when the driving force is equal to the frictional force. So there are two main ways of increasing a vehicle's maximum speed:

1) **Increasing the driving force**, e.g. by increasing the engine size.

2) **Reducing the frictional force**, e.g. making the body more streamlined.

Drag, Lift and Terminal Speed

Things **Falling** through **Air** or **Water** Reach a **Terminal Speed** too

When something's falling through air, the weight of the object is a constant force accelerating the object downwards.
Air resistance is a frictional force opposing this motion, which increases with speed.
So before a parachutist opens the parachute, exactly the same thing happens as with the car example:

1) A skydiver leaves
   a plane and will
   accelerate until the
   air resistance equals
   his **weight**.

2) He will then be
   travelling at a
   terminal speed.

But... the terminal speed of a person in free fall is too great to land without dying a horrible death.
The **parachute increases** the **air resistance massively**, which slows him down to a lower terminal speed:

3) Before reaching the
   ground he will **open
   his parachute**, which
   immediately **increases
   the air resistance** so it
   is now **bigger** than his
   weight.

4) This **slows him down**
   until his speed has
   dropped enough for the
   air resistance to be **equal
   to his weight** again. This
   new terminal speed is
   small enough for him to
   land safely.

A *v-t* graph of the skydiver looks like this. He
reaches terminal speed twice during his fall —
the second one is much slower than the first.

Warm-Up Questions

Q1 What forces limit the speed of a skier going down a slope?

Q2 What causes a lift force on a plane wing as it moves through air?

Q3 Suggest two ways in which the maximum speed of a car can be increased.

Q4 What conditions cause a terminal speed to be reached?

Exam Question

Q1 A space probe free-falls towards the surface of a planet.
The graph on the right shows the velocity of the probe as it falls.

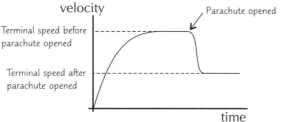

a) The planet does not have an atmosphere. Explain how you can tell this from the graph. [2 marks]

b) Sketch the velocity-time graph you would expect to see if the planet did have an atmosphere. [2 marks]

c) Explain the shape of the graph you have drawn. [3 marks]

You'll never understand this without going parachuting...*

*When you're doing questions about terminal velocity, remember the frictional forces reduce acceleration, not speed.
They usually don't slow an object down, apart from in the parachute example, where the skydiver is travelling faster just
before the parachute opens than the terminal velocity for the open parachute-skydiver combination.*

* No. 37 in a series of the 100 least convincing excuses for an interesting holiday.

Momentum and Impulse

These pages are about linear momentum — that's momentum in a straight line (not a circle).

Understanding **Momentum** Helps You Do **Calculations** on **Collisions**

The **momentum** of an object depends on two things — its **mass** and **velocity**.
The **product** of these two values is the momentum of the object.

| **momentum = mass × velocity** | or in symbols: | p **(in kg ms^{-1}) = m (in kg) × v (in ms^{-1})** |

*Remember, momentum is a vector quantity, so it has size **and** direction.*

Momentum is Always **Conserved**

You might see momentum referred to as 'linear momentum'. The other kind is 'angular momentum', but you don't need to know about that for now.

1) Assuming **no external forces** act, momentum is always **conserved**.
2) This means the **total momentum** of two objects **before** they collide **equals** the total momentum **after** the collision.
3) This is really handy for working out the **velocity** of objects after a collision (as you do...):

> **Example:** A skater of mass 75 kg and velocity 4.0 ms^{-1} collides with a stationary skater of mass 50 kg (to 2 s.f.). The two skaters join together and move off in the same direction. Calculate their velocity after impact.
>
> 4.0 ms^{-1} 0 ms^{-1}
> 75 kg   50 kg
> BEFORE
>
> v = ?
> 125 kg
> AFTER
>
> *Before you start a momentum calculation, always draw a quick sketch.*
>
> Momentum of skaters before = Momentum of skaters after
> (75 × 4.0) + (50 × 0) = 125v
> 300 = 125v
> So v = **2.4 ms^{-1}**

4) The same principle can be applied in **explosions**. E.g. if you fire an **air rifle**, the **forward momentum** gained by the pellet **equals** the **backward momentum** of the rifle, and you feel the rifle recoiling into your shoulder.

> **Example:** A bullet of mass 0.0050 kg is shot from a rifle at a speed of 200 ms^{-1}. The rifle has a mass of 4.0 kg. Calculate the velocity at which the rifle recoils.
>
> 4 kg × v 0.005 kg × 200 ms^{-1}
>
> Momentum before explosion = Momentum after explosion
> 0 = (0.0050 × 200) + (4.0 × v)
> 0 = 1 + 4v
> v = **−0.25 ms^{-1}**

Collisions Can be **Elastic** or **Inelastic**

An **elastic collision** is one where **momentum** is **conserved** and **kinetic energy** is **conserved** — i.e. no energy is dissipated as heat, sound, etc. If a collision is **inelastic** it means that some of the kinetic energy is converted into other forms during the collision. But **momentum is always conserved**.

> **Example:** A toy lorry (mass 2.0 kg) travelling at 3.0 ms^{-1} crashes into a smaller toy car (mass 800 g (to 2 s.f.)), travelling in the same direction at 2.0 ms^{-1}. The velocity of the lorry after the collision is 2.6 ms^{-1} in the same direction. Calculate the new velocity of the car and the total kinetic energy before and after the collision.
>
>
>
> 2kg   800g
> 3ms^{-1} 2ms^{-1} v = 2.6ms^{-1} v = ?
> BEFORE   AFTER
>
> Momentum before collision = Momentum after collision
> (2 × 3) + (0.8 × 2) = (2 × 2.6) + (0.8v)
> 7.6 = 5.2 + 0.8v
> 2.4 = 0.8v
> v = **3 ms^{-1}**
>
> Kinetic energy before = KE of lorry + KE of car
> = ½mv^2 (lorry) + ½mv^2 (car)
> = ½(2 × 3^2) + ½(0.8 × 2^2)
> = 9 + 1.6
> = **11 J (to 2 s.f.)**
>
> Kinetic energy after = ½(2 × 2.6^2) + ½(0.8 × 3^2)
> = 6.76 + 3.6
> = **10 J (to 2 s.f.)**
>
> *The difference in the two values is the amount of kinetic energy dissipated as heat or sound, or in damaging the vehicles — so this is an **inelastic** collision.*

Momentum and Impulse

Newton's 2nd Law Says That Force is the Rate of Change in Momentum...

The **rate of change of momentum** of an object is **directly proportional** to the **resultant force** which acts on the object.

So: $\boxed{F = \dfrac{\Delta(mv)}{\Delta t}}$ or $\boxed{F\Delta t = \Delta(mv)}$ (where *F* is constant)

Remember that acceleration is equal to the rate of change of velocity (page 52),
so if mass is constant then this formula gives you that mechanics favourite, $F = m \times a$.

Impulse = Change in Momentum

1) Newton's second law says **force = rate of change of momentum**, or $F = (mv - mu) \div t$

2) **Rearranging** Newton's 2nd law gives: ⟹
   Where **impulse** is defined as **force × time**, *Ft*.
   The units of impulse are **newton seconds**, Ns.

   $$Ft = mv - mu$$
   so **impulse = change in momentum**

   Where *v* is the final velocity and *u* is the initial velocity.

3) **Impulse** is the **area under** a **force-time graph** — this is really handy for solving problems where the force changes.

   Example: The graph shows the resultant force acting on a toy car.
   If the car is initially at rest, what is its momentum after 3 seconds?

   Impulse = change in momentum = *mv* – *mu*. The **initial momentum** (*mu*) is **zero** because the toy car is stationary to begin with. So, **impulse** = *mv*.

   Impulse is the **area under the graph**, so to find the **momentum** of the car after 3 seconds, you need to find the **area under the graph** between 0 and 3 seconds.

   Momentum = area under graph
   = (15 × 3) ÷ 2
   = **22.5 Ns**

4) The force of an impact is **increased** by **reducing** the impact time, e.g. the **less time** your foot is in contact with a football when kicking it, the **more force** you will kick it with (assuming the change in momentum is the same).

5) The **force** of an impact can be **reduced** by **increasing the time** of the impact, e.g. vehicle safety features.

6) In order to design vehicles **ethically**, manufacturers need to make sure the vehicles they produce are designed and fitted with features that help **protect people** in a crash.

- **Crumple zones** — the parts at the front and back of the car crumple up on impact. This causes the car to take longer to stop, increasing the impact time and decreasing the force on the passengers.

- **Seat belts** — these stretch slightly, increasing the time taken for the wearer to stop. This reduces the forces acting on the chest.

- **Air bags** — these also slow down passengers more gradually, and prevent them from hitting hard surfaces inside the car.

Warm-Up Questions

Q1 Give two examples of conservation of momentum in practice.

Q2 Describe what happens when a tiny object makes an elastic collision with a massive object, and why.

Q3 Describe how seat belts reduce the force acting on a car passenger in a collision.

Exam Questions

Q1 A ball of mass 0.60 kg moving at 5.0 ms⁻¹ collides with a larger stationary ball of mass 2.0 kg.
The smaller ball rebounds in the opposite direction at 2.4 ms⁻¹.

   a) Calculate the velocity of the larger ball immediately after the collision. [3 marks]

   b) State and explain whether this is an elastic or inelastic collision. Support your answer with calculations. [3 marks]

Q2 A toy train of mass 0.7 kg, travelling at 0.3 ms⁻¹, collides with a stationary toy carriage of mass 0.4 kg.
The two toys couple together. Calculate their new velocity. [3 marks]

Momentum'll never be an endangered species — it's always conserved...

*It seems odd to say that momentum's always conserved then tell you that impulse is the change in momentum. Impulse is just the change of momentum of one object, whereas conservation of momentum is talking about the **whole** system.*

Work and Power

As everyone knows, work in Physics isn't like normal work. It's harder. Work also has a specific meaning that's to do with movement and forces. You'll have seen this at GCSE — it just comes up in more detail for A level.

Work is Done Whenever Energy is Transferred

This table gives you some examples of **work being done** and the **energy changes** that happen.

1) Usually you need a force to move something because you're having to **overcome another force**.

2) The thing being moved has **kinetic energy** while it's **moving**.

3) The kinetic energy is transferred to **another form of energy** when the movement stops.

ACTIVITY	WORK DONE AGAINST	FINAL ENERGY FORM
Lifting up a box.	gravity	gravitational potential energy
Pushing a chair across a level floor.	friction	heat
Pushing two magnetic north poles together.	magnetic force	magnetic energy
Stretching a spring.	stiffness of spring	elastic potential energy

The word **'work'** in Physics means the **amount of energy transferred** from one form to another when a force causes a movement of some sort.

Work = Force × Distance

When a car tows a caravan, it applies a force to the caravan to move it to where it's wanted. To **find out** how much **work** has been **done**, you need to use the **equation**:

> **work done** (W) = **force causing motion** (F) × **distance moved** (s), or **$W = Fs$**
> ...where W is measured in joules (J), F is measured in newtons (N) and s is measured in metres (m).

Points to remember:

1) **Work** is the **energy** that's been **changed** from one form to another — it's not necessarily the **total** energy. E.g. moving a book from a low shelf to a higher one will increase its gravitational potential energy, but it had some potential energy to start with. Here, the **work done** would be the **increase** in potential energy, **not the total** potential energy.

2) Remember the distance needs to be measured in metres — if you have **distance in centimetres or kilometres**, you need to **convert** it to metres first.

3) The force **F** will be a **fixed** value in any calculations, either because it's **constant** or because it's the **average** force.

4) The equation assumes that the **direction of the force** is the **same** as the **direction of movement**.

5) The equation gives you the **definition** of the joule (symbol J):
'One joule is the work done when a force of 1 newton moves an object through a distance of 1 metre'.

The Force isn't Always in the Same Direction as the Movement

Sometimes the **direction of movement** is **different** from the **direction of the force**.

Example:

1) To **calculate the work done** in a situation like the one on the right, you need to consider the **horizontal** and **vertical components** of the **force**.

2) The only **movement** is in the **horizontal** direction. This means the **vertical force** is not causing any motion (and hence not doing any work) — it's just **balancing** out some of the **weight**, meaning there's a **smaller reaction force**.

3) The horizontal force is causing the motion — so to **calculate** the **work done**, this is the **only force** you need to consider. Which means we get:

direction of force on sledge

rosebud

direction of motion

> **$W = Fs\cos\theta$**

Where θ is the **angle** between the **direction of the force** and the **direction of motion**. See page 44 for more on resolving forces.

F

θ

$F\cos\theta$

Direction of motion

Work and Power

The **Area** Under a **Force-Displacement Graph** Tells You the **Work Done**

1) For a **variable force**, you can't just use the formula **W = Fs** — nightmare.

2) Luckily, plotting a **graph** of **force against distance moved** lets you calculate the work done by just finding the **area under the graph**.

3) You might need to **split it up** into sections that make shapes you can work out the area for, e.g. trapeziums.

The graph shows the force exerted by Tibalt the circus monkey as he cycled up a hill.

Work done in section A:
$40 \times \dfrac{300 + 150}{2} = 9000$ J

Work done in section B:
$40 \times \dfrac{200 + 150}{2} = 7000$ J

Total work done = **16 000 J**

Power = **Work Done** per **Second**

Power means many things in everyday speech, but in Physics (of course!) it has a special meaning. Power is the **rate of doing work** — in other words it is the **amount of energy transferred** from one form to another **per second**. You **calculate power** from this equation:

> **Power (P) = change in energy (or work done) (ΔW) / change in time (Δt), or $P = \dfrac{\Delta W}{\Delta t}$**
>
> ...where P is measured in watts (W), ΔW is measured in joules (J) and Δt is measured in seconds (s).

The **watt** (symbol W) is defined as a **rate of energy transfer** equal to **1 joule per second** (Js^{-1}).

Power is also **Force × Velocity**

Sometimes, it's **easier** to use **this version** of the power equation:

1) You know $P = \Delta W / \Delta t$.

2) You also know $\Delta W = F\Delta s$, which gives $P = F\Delta s / \Delta t$.

3) But $v = \Delta s / \Delta t$, which you can substitute into the above equation to give:

$$P = Fv$$

It's easier to use this if you're given speed in the question.

Warm-Up Questions

Q1 Write down the equation used to calculate work if the force and motion are in the same direction.

Q2 Write down the equation for work if the force is at an angle to the direction of motion.

Q3 What does the area under a force-distance graph represent?

Q4 Write down the equations relating a) power and work and b) power and speed.

Exam Questions

Q1 A traditional narrowboat is drawn by a horse walking along the towpath. The horse pulls the boat at a constant speed between two locks which are 1500 m apart. The tension in the rope is exactly 100 N (to 2 s.f.) at exactly 40° to the direction of motion.

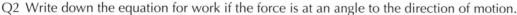

a) Calculate the work done on the boat. [2 marks]

b) The boat moves at 0.8 ms⁻¹. Calculate the power supplied to the boat in the direction of motion. [2 marks]

Q2 A motor is used to lift a 20 kg (to 2 s.f.) load a height of 3.0 m. (Take $g = 9.81$ Nkg⁻¹.)

a) Calculate the work done in lifting the load. [2 marks]

b) The speed of the load during the lift is 0.25 ms⁻¹. Calculate the power delivered by the motor. [2 marks]

Work — there's just no getting away from it...

Loads of equations to learn. Well, that's what you came here for, after all. Can't beat a good bit of equation-learning, as I've heard you say quietly to yourself when you think no one's listening. Aha, can't fool me. Ahahahahahahahahaha.

Conservation of Energy and Efficiency

Energy can never be lost. I repeat — energy can never be lost. Which is basically what I'm about to take up two whole pages saying. But that's, of course, because you need to do exam questions on this as well as understand the principle.

Learn the **Principle** of **Conservation** of **Energy**

The **principle of conservation of energy** says that:

Energy **cannot be created** or **destroyed**. Energy **can be transferred** from one form to another but the total amount of energy in a closed system will not change.

Total energy in = Total energy out

You can talk about how well energy is transferred in terms of **efficiency**.

$$\text{Efficiency} = \frac{\text{useful output power}}{\text{input power}}$$

Multiply by 100 to get the efficiency as a percentage.

You Need it for **Questions** about **Kinetic** and **Potential Energy**

The principle of conservation of energy nearly always comes up when you're doing questions about changes between kinetic and potential energy.

A quick reminder:

1) **Kinetic energy** is energy of anything **moving**, which you work out from $E_k = \frac{1}{2}mv^2$, where v is the velocity it's travelling at and m is its mass.

2) There are **different types of potential energy** — e.g. gravitational and elastic (see p.72).

3) **Gravitational potential energy** is the energy something gains if you lift it up. You work it out using: $\Delta E_p = mg\Delta h$, where m is the mass of the object, Δh is the height it is lifted and g is the gravitational field strength (9.81 Nkg^{-1} on Earth).

4) **Elastic strain energy** (elastic potential energy) is the energy you get in, say, a stretched rubber band or spring. You work this out using $E = \frac{1}{2}k\Delta l^2$, where Δl is the extension of the spring and k is the spring constant (p.70).

The energy you need to do things comes from your **food** — **chemical energy** inside the food is **converted** to other forms, e.g. **kinetic energy**. Be careful if you're trying to work out how much kinetic energy you can get from food though — a lot of the energy in food will actually be converted to other forms, e.g. **heat energy** to keep warm.

Examples: These pictures show you three examples of changes between kinetic and potential energy.

1) As Becky throws the ball upwards, kinetic energy is converted into gravitational potential energy. When it comes down again, that gravitational potential energy is converted back into kinetic energy.

2) As Dominic goes down the slide, gravitational potential energy is converted to kinetic energy.

3) As Simon bounces upwards from the trampoline, elastic potential energy is converted to kinetic energy, to gravitational potential energy. As he comes back down again, that gravitational potential energy is converted back to kinetic energy, to elastic potential energy, and so on.

In real life there are also frictional forces — Simon would have to exert some force from his muscles to keep jumping to the same height above the trampoline each time. Each time Simon jumps, some kinetic energy is converted to heat energy due to air resistance. You're usually told to ignore friction in exam questions — this means you can assume that the only forces are those that provide the potential or kinetic energy (in this example that's Simon's weight and the tension in the springs and trampoline material). If you're ignoring friction, you can say that the sum of the kinetic and potential energies is constant.

4) In a car crash, a lot of kinetic energy is transferred in a short space of time. Car safety features are designed to transfer some of this energy into other forms — this reduces the amount of energy transferred to the car passengers and other road users to help protect them. For example, crumple zones (see page 71) absorb some of the car's kinetic energy by deforming, seat belts absorb some of the passengers' kinetic energy by stretching.

Conservation of Energy and Efficiency

Use Conservation of Energy to Solve Problems

You need to be able to **use** conservation of mechanical energy (change in potential energy = change in kinetic energy) to solve problems. The classic example is the **simple pendulum**.

In a simple pendulum, you assume that all the mass is in the **bob** at the end.

Example: A simple pendulum has a mass of 720 g and a length of 50 cm (to 2 s.f.). It is pulled out to an angle of 30° (to 2 s.f.) from the vertical.

a) Find the gravitational potential energy stored in the pendulum bob.

You can work out the increase in height, Δh, of the end of the pendulum using trig.

Gravitational potential energy = $mg\Delta h$
$= 0.72 \times 9.81 \times (0.5 - 0.5 \cos 30°)$
$= 0.473...$ J
$= \textbf{0.47 J (to 2.s.f)}$

b) The pendulum is released. Find the maximum speed of the pendulum bob as it passes the vertical position.

To find the *maximum* speed, assume no air resistance, then $mg\Delta h = \frac{1}{2}mv^2$.

So $\frac{1}{2}mv^2 = 0.473...$

OR

Rearrange to find $v = \sqrt{\dfrac{2 \times 0.473...}{0.72}} = \textbf{1.1 ms}^{-1}$ **(to 2 s.f.)**

Cancel the ms and rearrange to give:
$v^2 = 2g\Delta h$
$= 2 \times 9.81 \times (0.5 - 0.5 \cos 30°)$
$= 1.31429...$
$v = \textbf{1.1 ms}^{-1}$ **(to 2 s.f.)**

You could be asked to apply this stuff to just about any situation in the exam. **Rollercoasters** are a bit of a favourite.

Warm-Up Questions

Q1 State the principle of conservation of energy.

Q2 What are the equations for calculating kinetic energy and gravitational potential energy?

Q3 Show that, if there's no air resistance and the mass of the string is negligible, the speed of a pendulum is independent of the mass of the bob.

Q4 An 1800 watt kettle transfers 1000 J per second to the water inside it. The rest is lost to other forms of energy. Calculate the efficiency of the kettle.

Exam Questions

Q1 A skateboarder is on a half-pipe. He lets the board run down one side of the ramp and up the other. The height of the ramp is 2 m. Take g as 9.81 Nkg^{-1}.

a) Assume that there is no friction. Calculate his speed at the lowest point of the ramp. [3 marks]

b) How high will he rise up the other side? [1 mark]

c) Real ramps are not frictionless, so what must the skater do to reach the top on the other side? [1 mark]

Q2 A 20.0 g rubber ball is released from a height of 8.0 m. (Assume that the effect of air resistance is negligible.)

a) Find the kinetic energy of the ball just before it hits the ground. [2 marks]

b) The ball strikes the ground and rebounds to a height of 6.5 m. Calculate how much energy is converted to heat and sound in the impact with the ground. [2 marks]

Energy is never lost — it just sometimes prefers the scenic route...

Right, done, on to the next question... remember to check your answers — I can't count the number of times I've forgotten to square the velocities or to multiply by the ½. I reckon it's definitely worth the extra minute to check.

Properties of Materials

Hooke's law applies to all materials, but only up to a point. For some materials that point is so tiny you wouldn't notice...

Density is Mass per Unit Volume

1) Density is a measure of the 'compactness' (for want of a better word) of a substance. It relates the mass of a substance to how much space it takes up.

$$\text{density} = \frac{\text{mass}}{\text{volume}} \qquad \rho = \frac{m}{V}$$

The **units** of **density** are g cm^{-3} or kg m^{-3} (N.B. $1 \text{ g cm}^{-3} = 1000 \text{ kg m}^{-3}$)

The symbol for density is a Greek letter rho (ρ) — it looks like a p but it isn't.

2) The density of an object depends on what it's made of. Density **doesn't vary** with **size or shape**.

3) The **average density** of an object determines whether it **floats** or **sinks** — a solid object will **float** on a fluid if it has a **lower density** than the **fluid**.

4) **Water** has a density of $\rho = 1 \text{ g cm}^{-3}$. So **1 cm³** of water has a mass of **1 g**.

Hooke's Law Says that Extension is Proportional to Force

If a **metal wire** is supported at the top and then a weight is attached to the bottom, the wire **stretches**. The weight pulls down with force **F**, producing an equal and opposite force at the support.

1) **Hooke's law** says that the extension of a stretched object, ΔL, is proportional to the load or force, **F**.

2) Hooke's law can be written:

$$F = k\Delta L$$

Where **k** is a constant called the **stiffness** of an object — it depends on the object being stretched. It is also called the **spring constant**.

If the markings on your measuring equipment are quite far apart, you can often interpolate between them. (E.g. if the length of the spring is halfway between the markings for 10 cm and 11 cm you could record it as 10.5 cm). But it's better to use something with a finer scale if you can.

3) **Springs** obey Hooke's Law — when you apply a **pair of opposite forces,** the **extension** (or **compression**) of a spring is **proportional** to the **force** applied.

4) Hooke's law works just as well for **compressive** forces as **tensile** forces. For a spring, **k** has the **same value** whether the forces are tensile or compressive (that's not true for all materials).

5) **Hooke's Law** doesn't just apply to metal **springs** and **wires** — most **other materials** obey it up to a point.

A material will only deform (stretch, bend, twist etc.) if there's a pair of opposite forces acting on it.

Hooke's Law Stops Working when the Force is Great Enough

There's a **limit** to the force you can apply for Hooke's law to stay true.

1) The graph shows force (or load) against extension for a **typical metal wire**.

2) The first part of the graph shows Hooke's law being obeyed — there's a **straight-line relationship** between **force** and **extension**.

3) When the force becomes great enough, the graph starts to **curve**. **Metals** generally obey Hooke's law up to the **limit of proportionality**, **P**.

4) The point marked **E** on the graph is called the **elastic limit**. If you increase the load past the elastic limit, the material will be **permanently stretched**. When all the force is removed, the material will be **longer** than at the start.

5) Be careful — there are some materials, like **rubber**, that only obey Hooke's law for **really small** extensions.

Properties of Materials

A Stretch can be Elastic or Plastic

Elastic

If a **deformation** is **elastic**, the material returns to its **original shape** and **size** once the forces are removed.

1) When the material is put under **tension**, the **atoms** of the material are **pulled apart** from one another.

2) Atoms can **move** small distances relative to their **equilibrium positions**, without actually changing position in the material.

3) Once the **load** is **removed**, the atoms **return** to their **equilibrium** distance apart.

Elastic deformation happens as long as the **elastic limit** of the object isn't reached.

Plastic

If a **deformation** is **plastic**, the material is **permanently stretched**.

1) Some atoms in the material move position relative to one another.

2) When the load is removed, the **atoms don't return** to their original positions.

3) An object stretched **past its elastic limit** shows plastic deformation.

Life in plastic, it's fantastic.

Energy is Always Conserved When Stretching

There's more about elastic strain energy on the next two pages (plus some formulas — hurrah!).

When a material is **stretched**, **work** has to be done in stretching the material.

1) If a deformation is **elastic**, all the work done is **stored** as **elastic strain energy** in the material.

2) When the stretching force is removed, this **stored energy** is **transferred** to **other forms** — e.g. an elastic band is stretched and then fired across a room.

3) If a deformation is **plastic**, work is done to **separate atoms**, and energy is **not** stored as strain energy (it's mostly dissipated as heat).

4) This fact is used in **transport design** — **crumple zones** are designed to deform **plastically** in a **crash**. Some energy goes into **changing the shape** of the vehicle's **metal body** (and so less is transferred to the people inside).

Warm-Up Questions

Q1 Write down the formula for calculating density. Will a material with a density of 0.8 g cm^{-3} float on water?

Q2 State Hooke's law, and explain what is meant by the elastic limit of a material.

Q3 From studying the force-extension graph for a material as weights are suspended from it, how can you tell:
   a) if Hooke's law is being obeyed,   b) if the elastic limit has been reached?

Q4 What is plastic behaviour of a material under load?

Q5 Explain how crumple zones protect passengers during a car crash.

PRACTICE QUESTIONS

Exam Questions

Q1 A metal guitar string stretches 4.0 mm when a 10.0 N force is applied to it.

   a) If the string obeys Hooke's law, calculate how far the string will stretch with a 15 N force applied to it. [1 mark]

   b) Calculate the stiffness, k, for this string in Nm^{-1}. [2 marks]

   c) The string is now stretched beyond its elastic limit. Describe what effect this will have on the string. [1 mark]

Q2 A rubber band is 6.0 cm long. When it is loaded with 2.5 N, its length becomes 10.4 cm. Further loading increases the length to 16.2 cm when the force is 5.0 N.

   Does the rubber band obey Hooke's law when the force on it is 5.0 N?
   Justify your answer with a suitable calculation. [2 marks]

Sod's law — if you don't learn it, it'll be in the exam...

Hooke's law was discovered (unsurprisingly) by Robert Hooke 350 years ago. Three bonus facts about Mr Hooke — he was the first person to use the word 'cell' (in terms of biology, not prisons), he helped Christopher Wren with his designs for St. Paul's Cathedral, and finally no-one actually knows what he looked like. How sad. Poor old Hooke.

Stress and Strain

How much a material stretches for a particular applied force depends on its dimensions. If you want to compare it to another material, you need to use stress and strain instead. A stress-strain graph is the same for any sample of a particular material — the size of the sample doesn't matter.

A Stress Causes a Strain

A material subjected to a pair of **opposite forces** might **deform** (i.e. **change shape**).
If the forces **stretch** the material, they're **tensile**. If the forces **squash** the material, they're **compressive**.

1) **Tensile stress** is defined as the **force applied**, *F*, divided by the **cross-sectional area**, *A*:

   $$\text{stress} = \frac{F}{A}$$

   The **units** of stress are Nm^{-2} or pascals, **Pa**.

2) **Tensile strain** is defined as the **change in length** (i.e. the **extension**), divided by the **original length** of the material:

   $$\text{strain} = \frac{\Delta L}{L}$$

   Strain has **no units**, it's just a **ratio** and is usually written as a **number**. It can also be written as a **percentage**, e.g. extending a 0.5 m wire by 0.02 m would produce a strain of $(0.02 \div 0.5) \times 100 = 4\,\%$.

3) It doesn't matter whether the forces producing the **stress** and **strain** are **tensile** or **compressive** — the **same equations** apply. The only difference is that you tend to think of **tensile** forces as **positive**, and **compressive** forces as **negative**.

A Stress Big Enough to **Break** the Material is Called the **Breaking Stress**

As a greater and greater tensile **force** is applied to a material, the **stress** on it **increases**.

1) The effect of the **stress** is to start to **pull** the **atoms apart** from one another.

2) Eventually the stress becomes **so great** that atoms **separate completely**, and the **material breaks**. This is shown by point **B** on the graph. The stress at which this occurs is called the **breaking stress**.

3) The point marked **UTS** on the graph is called the **ultimate tensile stress**. This is the **maximum stress** that the material can withstand.

4) Both **UTS** and **B** depend on conditions e.g. **temperature**.

5) **Engineers** have to consider the **UTS** and **breaking stress** of materials when designing a **structure** — e.g. they need to make sure the stress on a material won't reach the **UTS** when the **conditions change**.

Elastic Strain Energy is the **Area** under a **Force-Extension Graph**

1) **Work** has to be done to **stretch** a material.

2) **Before** the **elastic limit** is reached, **all** this **work done** in stretching is **stored** as **elastic strain energy** in the material.

3) On a **graph** of **force against extension**, the elastic strain energy is given by the **area under the graph**.

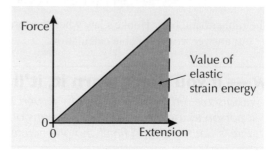

Stress and Strain

You can Calculate the Energy Stored in a Stretched Wire

Provided a material obeys Hooke's law, the **potential energy** stored inside it can be **calculated** quite easily.

1) The work done on the wire in stretching it is equal to the energy stored.

2) **Work done** equals **force × displacement**.

3) However, the **force** on the material **isn't constant**. It rises from zero up to force F.
To calculate the **work done**, use the **average force** between zero and F, i.e. ½F.

$$\text{work done} = \frac{1}{2}F \times \Delta L$$

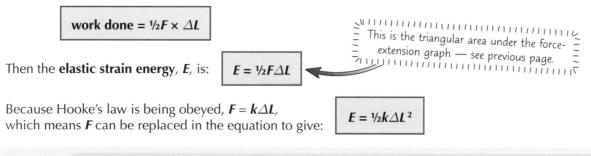

This is the triangular area under the force-extension graph — see previous page.

4) Then the **elastic strain energy**, E, is:

$$E = \frac{1}{2}F\Delta L$$

5) Because Hooke's law is being obeyed, $F = k\Delta L$,
which means F can be replaced in the equation to give:

$$E = \frac{1}{2}k\Delta L^2$$

> **Example:** A metal wire is 55.0 cm long. A force of 550 N is applied to the wire, and the wire stretches. The length of the stretched wire is 56.5 cm. Calculate the elastic strain energy stored in the wire.
>
> The extension of the wire is $\Delta L = 56.5$ cm $- 55.0$ cm $= 1.5$ cm $= 0.015$ m
> So the elastic strain energy $E = \frac{1}{2} \times F \times \Delta L$
> $\qquad\qquad = 1/2 \times 550 \times 0.015 = 4.125$ J $= \textbf{4.1 J (to 2 s.f.)}$

Warm-Up Questions

Q1 Write a definition for tensile stress.

Q2 Explain what is meant by the tensile strain on a material.

Q3 What is meant by the breaking stress of a material?

Q4 How can the elastic strain energy in a material under load be found from its force-extension graph?

Q5 The work done is usually calculated as force multiplied by displacement.
Explain why the work done in stretching a wire is ½$F\Delta L$.

PRACTICE QUESTIONS

Exam Questions

Q1 A steel wire is 2.00 m long. When a 300 N (to 3 s.f.) force is applied to the wire, it stretches 4.0 mm.
The wire has a circular cross-section with a diameter of 1.0 mm.

   a) Calculate the tensile stress in the wire. [2 marks]

   b) Calculate the tensile strain of the wire. [1 mark]

Q2 A copper wire (which obeys Hooke's law) is stretched by 3.0 mm when a force of 50.0 N is applied.

   a) Calculate the stiffness for this wire in Nm⁻¹. [2 marks]

   b) Calculate the value of the elastic strain energy in the stretched wire. [1 mark]

Q3 A pinball machine contains a spring which is used to fire a small, 12.0 g metal ball to start the game.
The spring has a spring constant of 40.8 Nm⁻¹. It is compressed by 5.00 cm and then released to fire the ball.

   Calculate the maximum possible kinetic energy of the ball. [3 marks]

UTS a laugh a minute, this stuff...

Here endeth the proper physics for this section — the rest of it's materials science (and I don't care what your exam boards say). It's all a bit "useful" for my liking. Calls itself a physics course... grumble... grumble... wasn't like this in my day... But to be fair — some of it's quite interesting, and there are some lovely graphs coming up on pages 75-77.

The Young Modulus

Busy chap, Thomas Young. He did this work on tensile stress as something of a sideline. Light was his main thing.
He proved that light behaved like a wave, explained how we see in colour and worked out what causes astigmatism.

The **Young Modulus** is Stress ÷ Strain

When you apply a **load** to stretch a material, it experiences a **tensile stress** and a **tensile strain**.

1) Up to the **limit of proportionality** (see p.70), the stress and strain of a material are proportional to each other.

2) So below this limit, for a particular material, stress divided by strain is a **constant**. This constant is called the **Young modulus, *E*.**

$$\text{Young modulus} = E = \frac{\text{tensile stress}}{\text{tensile strain}} = \frac{F \div A}{\Delta L \div L} = \frac{F\,L}{\Delta L\,A}$$

Where *F* = force in N, *A* = cross-sectional area in m²,
L = initial length in m and *ΔL* = extension in m.

3) The **units** of the Young modulus are the same as stress (**Nm⁻²** or pascals), since strain has no units.

4) The Young modulus is a measure of the **stiffness** of a material.
It is used by **engineers** to make sure the materials they are using can withstand sufficient forces.

To **Find** the Young Modulus, You need a **Very Long Wire**

PRACTICAL SKILLS

This is the experiment you're most likely to do in class:

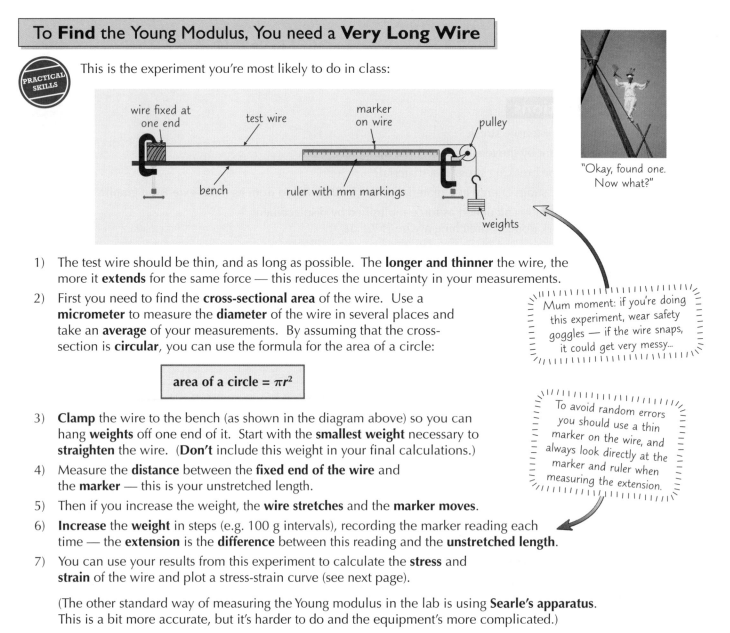

wire fixed at one end — test wire — marker on wire — pulley

bench — ruler with mm markings — weights

"Okay, found one. Now what?"

1) The test wire should be thin, and as long as possible. The **longer and thinner** the wire, the more it **extends** for the same force — this reduces the uncertainty in your measurements.

2) First you need to find the **cross-sectional area** of the wire. Use a **micrometer** to measure the **diameter** of the wire in several places and take an **average** of your measurements. By assuming that the cross-section is **circular**, you can use the formula for the area of a circle:

area of a circle = πr²

Mum moment: if you're doing this experiment, wear safety goggles — if the wire snaps, it could get very messy...

To avoid random errors you should use a thin marker on the wire, and always look directly at the marker and ruler when measuring the extension.

3) **Clamp** the wire to the bench (as shown in the diagram above) so you can hang **weights** off one end of it. Start with the **smallest weight** necessary to **straighten** the wire. (**Don't** include this weight in your final calculations.)

4) Measure the **distance** between the **fixed end of the wire** and the **marker** — this is your unstretched length.

5) Then if you increase the weight, the **wire stretches** and the **marker moves**.

6) **Increase** the **weight** in steps (e.g. 100 g intervals), recording the marker reading each time — the **extension** is the **difference** between this reading and the **unstretched length**.

7) You can use your results from this experiment to calculate the **stress** and **strain** of the wire and plot a stress-strain curve (see next page).

(The other standard way of measuring the Young modulus in the lab is using **Searle's apparatus**. This is a bit more accurate, but it's harder to do and the equipment's more complicated.)

The Young Modulus

Use a **Stress-Strain Graph** to Find **E**

You can plot a **graph** of **stress against strain** from your results.

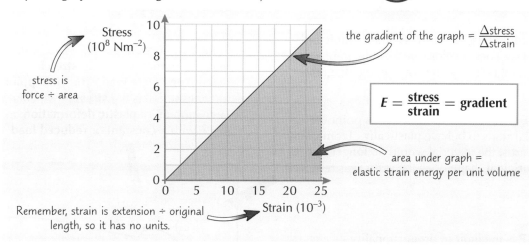

the gradient of the graph $= \dfrac{\Delta \text{stress}}{\Delta \text{strain}}$

$$E = \frac{\text{stress}}{\text{strain}} = \text{gradient}$$

area under graph = elastic strain energy per unit volume

Remember, strain is extension ÷ original length, so it has no units.

1) The **gradient** of the graph gives the Young modulus, **E**.

2) The **area under the graph** gives the **strain energy** (or energy stored) per unit volume, i.e. the energy stored per 1 m³ of wire.

3) The stress-strain graph is a **straight line** provided that Hooke's law is obeyed, so you can also calculate the energy per unit volume (Jm⁻³) as:

> **energy per unit vol = ½ × stress × strain**

Example: The stress-strain graph above is for a thin metal wire. Find the Young modulus of the wire from the graph.

E = change in stress ÷ change in strain = gradient

The gradient of the graph $= \dfrac{\Delta \text{stress}}{\Delta \text{strain}} = \dfrac{10 \times 10^8}{25 \times 10^{-3}}$

$$= \mathbf{4 \times 10^{10}\ Nm^{-2}}$$

Warm-Up Questions

Q1 Define the Young modulus for a material. What are the units for the Young modulus?

Q2 Describe an experiment to find the Young modulus of a test wire. Explain why a thin test wire should be used.

Q3 What is given by the area contained under a stress-strain graph?

Exam Questions

Q1 A steel wire is stretched elastically. For a load of 80.0 N, the wire extends by 3.6 mm.
The original length of the wire was 2.50 m and its average diameter is 0.60 mm.
Calculate the value of the Young modulus for steel. [4 marks]

Q2 Two wires, A and B, are stretched elastically under a load of 50.0 N. The original length and the extension of both wires under this load are the same. The Young modulus of wire A is found to be 7.0×10^{10} Nm⁻².
The cross-sectional area of wire B is half that of wire A. Calculate the Young modulus of wire B. [2 marks]

Q3 The Young modulus for copper is 1.3×10^{11} Nm⁻².

a) The stress on a copper wire is 2.6×10^8 Nm⁻². Calculate the strain on the wire. [2 marks]

b) The load applied to the copper wire is 100 N (to 3 s.f.). Calculate the cross-sectional area of the wire. [2 marks]

c) Calculate the strain energy per unit volume for this loaded wire. [2 marks]

Learn that experiment — it's important...

Getting back to the good Dr Young... As if ground-breaking work in light, the physics of vision and materials science wasn't enough, he was also a well-respected physician, a linguist and an Egyptologist. He was one of the first to try to decipher the Rosetta stone (he didn't get it right, but nobody's perfect). Makes you feel kind of inferior, doesn't it...

Stress-Strain and Force-Extension Graphs

I hope the stresses and strains of this section aren't getting to you too much.
Don't worry, though — there's just these two pages to go before you're on to the electrifying world of electricity.

There are **Three Important Points** on a **Stress-Strain Graph**

In the exam you could be given a **stress-strain graph** and asked to **interpret** it. Luckily, most stress-strain graphs share **three** important points — as shown in the **diagram**.

Point **Y** is the **yield point** — here the material suddenly starts to **stretch** without any extra load. The **yield point** (or yield stress) is the **stress** at which a large amount of **plastic deformation** takes place with a **constant** or **reduced load**.

Point **E** is the **elastic limit** — at this point the material starts to behave **plastically**. From point E onwards, the material would **no longer** return to its **original shape** once the stress was removed.

Point **P** is the **limit of proportionality** — after this, the graph is no longer a straight line but starts to **bend**. At this point, the material **stops** obeying **Hooke's law**, but would still **return** to its **original shape** if the stress was removed.

Before point **P**, the graph is a **straight line** through the **origin**. This shows that the material is obeying Hooke's law (page 70). The **gradient** of the line is constant — it's the **Young modulus** (see pages 74-75).

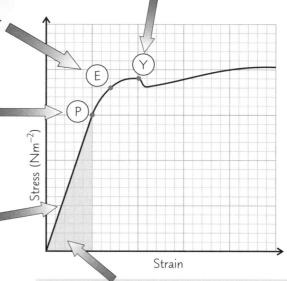

The **area** under this part of the graph gives the **energy stored** in the **material per unit volume** as it is stretched to point **P**. (see page 75).

Stress-Strain Graphs for **Brittle** Materials **Don't Curve**

The graph shown below is typical of a **brittle** material.

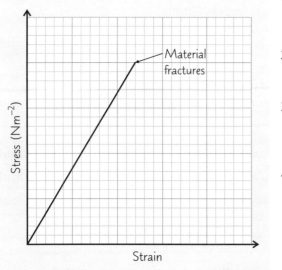

1) The graph starts the same as the one above — with a **straight line through the origin**. So brittle materials also obey **Hooke's law**.

2) However, when the **stress** reaches a certain point, the material suddenly **fractures** (breaks) — it **doesn't deform plastically**.

3) A **chocolate bar** is an example of a brittle material — you can break chunks of chocolate off the bar without the whole thing changing shape.

4) **Ceramics** (e.g. **glass** and **pottery**) are brittle too — they tend to shatter.

Stress-Strain and Force-Extension Graphs

Force-Extension Graphs Are Similar to Stress-Strain Graphs

You met force-extension graphs on page 70.

1) Force-extension graphs look a lot like **stress-strain** graphs, but they show slightly different things.

2) Force-extension graphs are **specific** for the tested **object** and **depend on its dimensions**. Stress-strain graphs describe the **general behaviour** of a **material**, because stress and strain are **independent of the dimensions**.

3) You can plot a force-extension graph of what happens when you gradually **remove** a **force** from an object. The **unloading** line doesn't always match up with the **loading** line though.

A force-extension graph for a metal wire

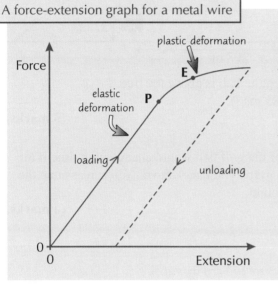

1) This graph is for a metal wire that has been stretched beyond its **limit of proportionality (P)** so the graph starts to **curve**.

2) When the load is **removed**, the **extension decreases**.

3) The unloading line is **parallel** to the loading line because the stiffness *k* is still the same (since the forces between the atoms are the same as they were during the loading).

4) But because the wire was stretched beyond its **elastic limit (E)** and deformed **plastically**, it has been **permanently stretched**. This means the unloading line doesn't go through the origin.

5) The **area** between the two lines is the **work done** to permanently deform the wire.

Of course, if you apply a big enough load to <u>fracture</u> the object, you can't draw an unloading line — you just get a force-extension graph like one of these graphs.

Warm-Up Questions

Q1 What is the difference between the limit of proportionality and the elastic limit?

Q2 Describe what happens at the yield point.

Q3 A metal wire is stretched beyond its elastic limit. Why does the unloading line on the force-extension graph for the wire not go through the origin?

PRACTICE QUESTIONS

Exam Questions

Q1 Hardened steel is a hard, brittle form of steel made by heating it up slowly and then quenching it in cold water.

a) State what is meant by the term brittle. [1 mark]

b) Sketch a stress-strain graph for hardened steel. [2 marks]

Q2 The diagram shows a stress-strain graph for a nylon thread.

a) State the yield stress for nylon. [1 mark]

b) Calculate the tensile force on the thread at a strain of 0.2, given that the thread has a cross-sectional area of $1.8 \times 10^{-4} \, \text{m}^{-2}$. [1 mark]

c) Calculate the elastic strain energy stored by the thread at a strain of 0.2, given that the unstressed length of the nylon thread is 40 cm. [2 marks]

My sister must be brittle — she's always snapping...

It's the end of the section on materials, but don't shed a tear — there's four more pages of extra practice coming up. You can always come back and re-read these pages too — it's a good idea, even if you can do all of the practice questions.

Extra Exam Practice

Phew — that's <u>Sections 4 and 5</u> all sewn up. Time to put it all into practice with a few mixed questions.

- Have a look at this example of how to answer a tricky exam question.
- Then check how much you've understood from Sections 4 and 5 by having a go at the questions on the next page.

---

1   A golf ball is struck off a tee at an angle of 42° to the horizontal. The ball has an initial velocity of 60.0 ms⁻¹, as shown in **Figure 1**.

Figure 1

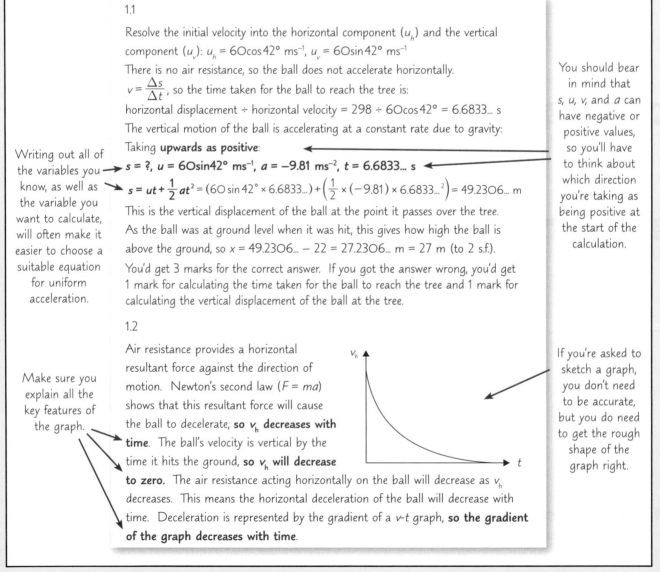

60.0 ms⁻¹

42°

298 m

x m

22 m

1.1   The golf ball flies directly over a tree. The tree is 22 m tall, and is a distance of 298 m from the tee. Calculate the vertical distance, x, between the ball and the tree when the ball is above the tree. Assume that no air resistance acts on the ball (g = 9.81 ms⁻²).

(3 marks)

1.2   Sketch a graph to show how the horizontal velocity of the golf ball would change with time if air resistance were considered. Explain the shape of the graph you have drawn. You can assume the golf ball is falling vertically by the time it hits the ground.

(4 marks)

1.1

Resolve the initial velocity into the horizontal component (u_h) and the vertical component (u_v): $u_h = 60\cos 42°$ ms⁻¹, $u_v = 60\sin 42°$ ms⁻¹

There is no air resistance, so the ball does not accelerate horizontally.

$v = \frac{\Delta s}{\Delta t}$, so the time taken for the ball to reach the tree is:

horizontal displacement ÷ horizontal velocity = 298 ÷ 60 cos 42° = 6.6833... s

The vertical motion of the ball is accelerating at a constant rate due to gravity:

Taking **upwards as positive:**

> *Writing out all of the variables you know, as well as the variable you want to calculate, will often make it easier to choose a suitable equation for uniform acceleration.*

$s = ?$, $u = 60\sin 42°$ ms⁻¹, $a = -9.81$ ms⁻², $t = 6.6833...$ s

$s = ut + \frac{1}{2}at^2 = (60\sin 42° \times 6.6833...) + \left(\frac{1}{2} \times (-9.81) \times 6.6833...^2\right) = 49.2306...$ m

This is the vertical displacement of the ball at the point it passes over the tree. As the ball was at ground level when it was hit, this gives how high the ball is above the ground, so $x = 49.2306... - 22 = 27.2306...$ m = 27 m (to 2 s.f.).

You'd get 3 marks for the correct answer. If you got the answer wrong, you'd get 1 mark for calculating the time taken for the ball to reach the tree and 1 mark for calculating the vertical displacement of the ball at the tree.

> *You should bear in mind that s, u, v, and a can have negative or positive values, so you'll have to think about which direction you're taking as being positive at the start of the calculation.*

1.2

Air resistance provides a horizontal resultant force against the direction of motion. Newton's second law ($F = ma$) shows that this resultant force will cause the ball to decelerate, **so v_h decreases with time**. The ball's velocity is vertical by the time it hits the ground, **so v_h will decrease to zero**. The air resistance acting horizontally on the ball will decrease as v_h decreases. This means the horizontal deceleration of the ball will decrease with time. Deceleration is represented by the gradient of a v-t graph, **so the gradient of the graph decreases with time.**

> *Make sure you explain all the key features of the graph.*

v_h

t

> *If you're asked to sketch a graph, you don't need to be accurate, but you do need to get the rough shape of the graph right.*

Extra Exam Practice

2 A child has a toy gun that fires 1.2 g foam pellets. The toy works by compressing a spring. When the spring is released, the energy stored in the spring is transferred to the kinetic energy of the pellet with an efficiency of 92%. The child holds the gun still, before shooting a pellet out of the first floor window of his house and onto the lawn below, as shown in **Figure 2**. You may assume that the pellet does not experience any air resistance.

Figure 2

2.1 The spring in the toy has a spring constant of 275 Nm⁻¹. It is compressed by 4.0 cm before it is released. Show that the speed, v, of a pellet immediately after it has been pushed out of the gun is 18 ms⁻¹. You may assume that the spring obeys Hooke's law as it is compressed.

(3 marks)

2.2 The pellet applies a force of 4.1 N to the gun, causing the gun to recoil. Calculate the time over which this force is applied to the gun.

(2 marks)

2.3 Show that the time taken for the pellet to travel from the gun to the lawn is 1.7 s. ($g = 9.81$ ms⁻²)

(3 marks)

2.4 Calculate the speed and the angle from the horizontal at which the pellet hits the lawn.

(3 marks)

2.5 The child fires a second pellet. A wind exerts a force of 5.2×10^{-3} N on the pellet at an angle of 32° to the horizontal, as shown in **Figure 3**. Calculate the magnitude of the resultant force acting on the pellet during its flight.

(2 marks)

Figure 3

3 In an experiment, a motor is used to pull a 2.4 kg box up a rough ramp, as shown in **Figure 4**.

Figure 4

The box is pulled to the top of the ramp in 2.2 s. It accelerates at a constant rate of 14.6 ms⁻² during this time. The frictional force, F, acting on the box as it moves is given by $F = \mu R$, where μ is the coefficient of friction of the ramp, and R is the normal contact force acting on the box. The ramp's coefficient of friction is 0.81.

3.1 Calculate the average output power of the motor during this time.

(4 marks)

3.2 The experiment is repeated, but this time, the motor is turned off when the box has travelled a distance of d m up the ramp. The box comes to a halt just as it reaches the top of the ramp. Calculate the value of d.

(4 marks)

Extra Exam Practice

In a second experiment, a light inextensible string is used to attach the same box to a mass. The string is passed over a pulley, and the mass is held at a height, h, above the ground, as shown in **Figure 5**. The box and the mass have weights of W_1 and W_2 respectively. $W_1 < W_2$, so when the mass is released, the box moves upwards and the mass moves downwards. They both move with an acceleration, a. You can assume that the pulley is frictionless and that air resistance is negligible.

3.3 Show that $a = \dfrac{(W_2 - W_1)g}{W_1 + W_2}$.

(3 marks)

A motor is attached to the pulley when the mass is on the ground. The motor has an electrical power rating of 5.4 W and an efficiency of 78%. When it is switched on, the pulley is forced to spin, causing the box to be lowered to the ground (and the mass to be lifted) at a constant speed. $W_2 = 26.5$ N, and $h = 82$ cm.

3.4 Calculate how long the motor needs to be on for before the box hits the ground.

(4 marks)

Figure 5

4 A wooden mobile for a baby's crib is shown in **Figure 6**. The mobile is made up of four cylindrical rods that are attached to four sides of a central cube. Identical spheres, moons and stars are attached to each of the four rods using wire. The mobile is suspended by a piece of string that is attached to the centre of the top surface of the cube. The rods are all horizontal when the mobile is hung up by the piece of string. The components of the mobile are all made from wood with a uniform density of 0.55×10^3 kg m^{-3}.
Table 1 shows the weight of some of the mobile's components.

Table 1

Component	Weight / N
Central cube	1.165
Rod A, rod D	0.120
Rod B, rod C	0.150
Moon	0.025
Wire	Negligible

4.1 Each sphere has a circumference of 9.2 cm. Show that the weight of a sphere is 0.071 N.

(3 marks)

4.2 Calculate the weight of one of the wooden stars.

(3 marks)

4.3 The piece of string that the mobile is suspended by has a diameter of 2.0 mm. The Young modulus of the string is 2.2 GPa. Calculate how much the string extends by when the mobile is hung up, as a percentage of the string's original length. You may assume that the string is cylindrical.

(3 marks)

Extra Exam Practice

5 A student is doing an experiment to determine the Young modulus of a wire. She uses the apparatus shown in **Figure 7**. Two identical wires are suspended from a rigid support. Each wire is attached to a metal frame, which are loosely connected by three cross supports. A spirit level is attached to one of the cross supports.

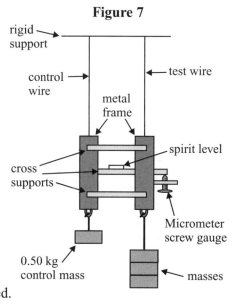

Figure 7

At the start of the experiment, both metal frames are loaded with a 0.50 kg mass, and the micrometer screw gauge is adjusted so that the spirit level lies horizontally. The reading on the micrometer, d_0, is recorded. Masses are then added one at a time to the metal frame of the test wire, whilst the control mass is kept constant. Each time an extra mass is added, the metal frame attached to the test wire moves down slightly, causing the spirit level to deviate from the horizontal. The micrometer is adjusted so that the spirit level is horizontal, and the reading on the micrometer, d, is recorded.

5.1 Explain how the apparatus in **Figure 7** reduces the effects of any thermal expansion of the wire during the experiment and the effects of any kinks in the wire. In your answer, you should include an explanation of how these would each affect the value obtained for the Young modulus if they were not accounted for.

(3 marks)

The student plots a stress-strain graph for the test wire, and labels point E (the elastic limit) and point P (the limit of proportionality). The lines of best fit are shown in **Figure 8**.

5.2 Describe how the student could have calculated the values of stress and strain for each set of results in order to plot them on the graph. State any extra equipment she would need.

(3 marks)

Figure 8

5.3 Describe what the elastic limit is. Suggest how the student could have estimated the position of point E from her experiment in order to plot it on her graph of results.

(3 marks)

5.4 Calculate the Young modulus of the test wire.

(1 mark)

5.5 At the start of the experiment, the test wire had a length of 750 mm and a diameter of 0.40 mm. Calculate the total work done on the test wire to produce a strain of 0.11%.

You may assume that the volume of the test wire is constant throughout the experiment.

(3 marks)

Current, Potential Difference and Resistance

You wouldn't reckon there was that much to know about electricity... just plug something in, and bosh — electricity. Ah well, never mind the age of innocence — here are all the gory details...

Current is the Rate of Flow of Charge

1) The **current** in a **wire** is like **water** flowing in a **pipe**. The **amount** of water that flows depends on the **flow rate** and the **time**. It's the same with electricity — **current is the rate of flow of charge**.

$$\Delta Q = I\Delta t \text{ or } I = \frac{\Delta Q}{\Delta t}$$

Where ΔQ is the charge in coulombs, I is the current in amperes and Δt is the time taken in seconds.

Remember that conventional current flows from + to -, the opposite way from electron flow.

2) The **coulomb** is the unit of **charge**.

One **coulomb** (C) is defined as the **amount of charge** that passes in **1 second** if the **current** is **1 ampere** (A).

3) You can measure the current flowing through a part of a circuit using an **ammeter**. Remember — you always need to attach an ammeter in **series** (so that the current through the ammeter is the same as the current through the component — see page 92).

Potential Difference is the Energy per Unit Charge

1) To make electric charge flow through a conductor, you need to do work on it.
2) **Potential difference** (p.d.), or **voltage**, is defined as the **work done** (energy converted) **per unit charge moved**.

$$V = \frac{W}{Q}$$

W is the work done in joules.

Back to the 'water analogy' again. The p.d. is like the pressure that's forcing water along the pipe.

Resistor

6 V

Here you do 6 J of work moving each coulomb of charge through the resistor, so the p.d. across it is 6 V. The energy gets converted to heat.

3) You can measure the potential difference across a component using a **voltmeter**.
4) Remember, the potential difference across components in parallel is **the same**, so the **voltmeter** should be connected in **parallel** with the component.

Definition of the Volt
The **potential difference** across a component is **1 volt** when you convert **1 joule** of energy moving **1 coulomb** of charge through the component.

$$1\,V = 1\,JC^{-1}$$

Everything has Resistance

1) If you put a **potential difference** (p.d.) across an **electrical component**, a **current** will flow.
2) **How much** current you get for a particular **p.d.** depends on the **resistance** of the component.
3) You can think of a component's **resistance** as a **measure** of how **difficult** it is to get a **current** to **flow** through it.

Mathematically, **resistance** is: $R = \frac{V}{I}$

This equation **defines** resistance.

Unless told otherwise, you can assume voltmeters are infinitely resistant, and that ammeters have no resistance.

4) **Resistance** is measured in **ohms** (Ω).

A component has a resistance of **1 Ω** if a **potential difference** of **1 V** makes a **current** of **1 A** flow through it.

Current, Potential Difference and Resistance

For an **Ohmic Conductor**, *R* is a **Constant**

1) A chap called **Ohm** did most of the early work on resistance.
   He developed a rule to **predict** how the **current** would **change** as the applied
   potential difference increased, for **certain types** of conductor.

2) The rule is now called **Ohm's law** and the conductors that **obey** it (mostly metals) are
   called **ohmic conductors**.

Provided the **physical conditions**, such as **temperature**, remain **constant**, the **current**
through an ohmic conductor is **directly proportional** to the **potential difference** across it.

$$I \propto V$$

1) This graph shows what happens if you plot
   current against voltage for an ohmic conductor.

2) As you can see it's a **straight-line** graph
   — **doubling** the **p.d.** **doubles** the **current**.

3) What this means is that the **resistance** is
   constant — $V \div I$ is always a fixed value.

4) Often **factors** such as **light level** or **temperature** will have
   a **significant effect** on resistance (the resistivity changes,
   see page 86), so you need to remember that Ohm's law is
   only true for **ohmic conductors** under **constant physical
   conditions**, e.g. temperature.

5) Ohm's law is a **special case** — lots of components aren't
   ohmic conductors and have characteristic current-voltage
   (*I–V*) graphs of their very own (see pages 84-85).

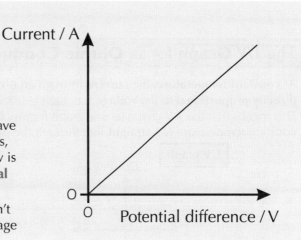

Warm-Up Questions

Q1 Describe in words how current and charge are related.

Q2 Define the coulomb.

Q3 Define potential difference.

Q4 Give the values of resistance that we assume voltmeters and ammeters to have.

Q5 Name one environmental factor likely to alter the resistance of a component.

Q6 What is special about an ohmic conductor?

Exam Questions

Q1 A battery delivers 4500 C of electric charge to a circuit in 10.0 minutes. Calculate the average current. [1 mark]

Q2 An electric motor runs off a 12 V d.c. supply.
Calculate how much electric charge will pass through the motor when it transfers 120 J of energy. [2 marks]

Q3 A current of 12 amps flows through an ohmic conductor when a potential difference of 2.0 V is applied across it.
Assume the temperature of the conductor remains constant.

a) Calculate the resistance of the conductor. [1 mark]

b) Calculate the current through the conductor when the potential difference across it is 35 V. [1 mark]

c) Sketch the *I-V* graph for the conductor when potential differences of up to 35 V are applied to it. [1 mark]

I can't even be bothered to make the current joke...

*Talking of currant jokes, I saw this bottle of wine the other day called 'raisin d'être' — 'raison d'être' of course meaning
'reason for living', but spelled slightly different to make 'raisin', meaning 'grape'. Ho ho. Chuckled all the way home.*

I/V Characteristics

Woohoo — real physics. This stuff's actually kind of interesting.

I/V Graphs Show how Resistance Varies

1) The term '**I/V characteristic**' refers to a **graph** of *I* **against** *V* which shows how the **current** (*I*) flowing through a **component changes** as the **potential difference** (*V*) across it is increased.

2) This **diagram** shows the type of **circuit** used to obtain a characteristic *I/V* graph for a component.

You could also be asked about a **V/I graphs**. They're pretty similar, but with *V* plotted against *I*. The **resistance** at a point on the graph is simply *V/I* at that point.

The I/V Graph for an Ohmic Conductor is a Straight Line through the Origin

At **constant temperature**, the **current** through an **ohmic conductor** (e.g. metals) is **directly proportional** to the **voltage** (i.e. their resistance is constant, see page 83). This means that the *I/V* characteristic graph for an ohmic conductor at a constant temperature is a **straight line** through the **origin**.

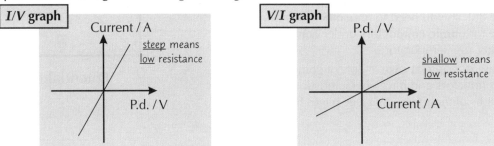

The I/V Characteristic for a Filament Lamp is a Curve

The *I/V* characteristic for a **filament lamp** is a **curve** that starts **steep** but gets **shallower** as the **voltage rises**.

The **filament** in a lamp is just a **coiled-up** length of **metal wire**, so you might think it should have the **same characteristic graph** as a **metallic conductor**. It doesn't because it **gets hot**. **Current** flowing through the lamp **increases** its **temperature**.

The **resistance** of a **metal increases** as the **temperature increases**.

The *V/I* graph for a filament lamp is a curve that starts shallow and gets steeper as the current and voltage increase.

Semiconductors are Used in Sensors

Semiconductors are **nowhere near** as good at **conducting** electricity as **metals**. This is because there are far, far **fewer charge carriers** available. However, if **energy** is supplied to the semiconductor, **more charge carriers** can be **released**. This means that they make **excellent sensors** for detecting **changes** in their **environment**.

You need to know about the **two** semiconductor components on the next page — **thermistors** and **diodes**.

I/V Characteristics

The Resistance of a Thermistor Depends on Temperature

1) A **thermistor** is a **resistor** with a **resistance** that depends on its **temperature**.

2) You only need to know about **NTC** thermistors — NTC stands for 'Negative Temperature Coefficient'.

3) This means that the **resistance decreases** as the **temperature goes up**.

The *I/V* characteristic graph for an NTC thermistor curves upwards.

As the voltage increases, the current increases. More current leads to an increase in temperature and so a decrease in resistance. This in turn means more current can flow, so the graph curves upwards.

As usual, the gradient of the V/I graph does the opposite.

Warming the thermistor gives more **electrons** enough **energy** to **escape** from their atoms. This means that there are **more charge carriers** available, so the resistance is lower.

Diodes Only Let Current Flow in One Direction

Diodes (including light emitting diodes (LEDs)) are designed to let **current flow** in **one direction** only. You don't need to be able to explain how they work, just what they do.

1) **Forward bias** is the **direction** in which the **current** is **allowed to flow**.

2) **Most** diodes require a **threshold voltage** of about **0.6 V** in the **forward direction** before they will conduct.

3) In **reverse bias**, the **resistance** of the diode is **very high** and the current that flows is **very tiny**.

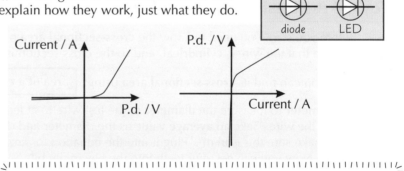

Diodes let current flow in the direction that the triangle in the circuit symbol points.

Warm-Up Questions

Q1 Sketch the circuit used to determine the *I/V* characteristics of a component.

Q2 Why does an *I/V* graph curve for a filament lamp?

Q3 Draw an *I/V* characteristic graph for a diode.

Exam Questions

Q1 a) Describe the shape of a current-voltage characteristic graph for a filament lamp. [1 mark]

b) Explain the changes in the gradient of the graph as the current increases. [2 marks]

Q2 Explain, with reference to charge carriers, how an NTC thermistor connected in a circuit can be used as a temperature sensor. [3 marks]

You light up my world like an LED — with One Directional current...

Learn the graphs on these two pages, and check that you can explain them. Remember that a temperature increase causes an increase in resistance in a filament lamp, but a decrease in resistance in a thermistor.

Resistivity and Superconductivity

Resistance is all well and good, but it depends on the size of the thing doing the resisting. If you want to compare two materials, you need a quantity that doesn't depend on size. Enter 'resistivity'...

Three Things Determine Resistance

If you think about a nice, **simple electrical component**, like a **length of wire**, its **resistance** depends on:

1) **Length (*l*)**. The **longer** the wire, the **more difficult** it is to make a **current flow**.

2) **Area (*A*)**. The **wider** the wire, the **easier** it is to make a current flow.

3) **Resistivity (*ρ*)**, which **depends** on the **material**. The **structure** may make it easy or difficult for charge to flow. In general, resistivity depends on **environmental factors** as well, like **temperature** and **light intensity**.

| The **resistivity** of a material is defined as the **resistance** of a **1 m length** with a **1 m² cross-sectional area**. It is measured in **ohm-metres (Ωm)**. | $\rho = \dfrac{RA}{l}$ | *ρ* (Greek letter 'rho') = resistivity, *A* = cross-sectional area in m², *l* = length in m |

Typical values for the **resistivity** of **conductors** are **really small**, e.g. for **copper** (at 25 °C) $\rho = 1.72 \times 10^{-8}$ Ωm.

Example: A cross-section of Mr T's gold medallion is shown below. Jess found its length to be 0.500 cm and its resistance to be 1.1×10^{-8} Ω. The resistivity of gold is 2.2×10^{-8} Ωm. Is the medallion real gold?

10 cm
10 cm

Convert all the lengths into metres.

The cross-sectional area of the medallion = 0.1 m × 0.1 m = 0.01 m². Length = *l* = 0.005 m

So the resistivity = $\rho = \dfrac{RA}{l} = \dfrac{(1.1 \times 10^{-8} \times 0.01)}{0.005} = \mathbf{2.2 \times 10^{-8} \, \Omega m}$

So Mr T's gold is the real deal.

To Find the Resistivity of a Wire you Need to Find its Resistance

PRACTICAL SKILLS

Before you start, you need to know the **cross-sectional area** of the test wire. Assume that the wire is **cylindrical**, and so the cross-section is **circular**.

Then you can find its **cross-sectional area** using: **area of a circle = πr^2**

Use a **micrometer** to measure the **diameter** of the test wire in at least **three** different points along the wire. Take an **average** value as the diameter and divide by **2** to get the **radius** (make sure this is in m). Plug it into the equation for cross-sectional area and... **ta da**. Now you can get your teeth into the electricity bit...

Remember, a micrometer, sometimes called a micrometer caliper, is used to measure very small distances.

1) The **test wire** should be **clamped** to a ruler with the circuit attached to the wire where the ruler reads zero.

2) Attach the **flying lead** to the test wire — the lead is just a wire with a crocodile clip at the end to allow connection to any point along the test wire.

3) Record the **length** of the test wire **connected** in the circuit, the **voltmeter reading** and the **ammeter reading**.

4) Use your readings to calculate the **resistance** of the length of wire, using: $R = \dfrac{V}{I}$

power supply
flying lead
length
ruler
test wire

5) Repeat this measurement and calculate an average resistance for the length.

6) Repeat for several **different** lengths, for example between 0.10 and 1.00 m.

7) Plot your results on a graph of **resistance** against **length**, and draw a **line of best fit** (see page 101).

> The **gradient** of the line of best fit is equal to $\dfrac{R}{l} = \dfrac{\rho}{A}$. So **multiply** the **gradient** of the line of best fit by the **cross-sectional area** of the wire to find the resistivity of the wire material.

8) The **resistivity** of a material depends on its **temperature**, so you can only find the resistivity of a material **at a certain temperature**. Current flowing in the test wire can cause its temperature to increase, which can lead to random errors and invalid results (see p.99). Try to keep the temperature of the test wire **constant**, e.g. by only having small currents flow through the wire.

Resistivity and Superconductivity

Superconductors Have Zero Resistivity

1) Normally, all materials have **some resistivity**
— even really good conductors like silver and copper.

2) That resistance means that whenever electricity flows through them,
they **heat up**, and some of the electrical energy is **wasted** as thermal energy (heat).

3) You can **lower** the resistivity of many materials like metals by **cooling them down**.

4) If you **cool** some materials (e.g. mercury) down to below a '**transition temperature**',
their **resistivity disappears entirely** and they become a **superconductor**.

5) Without any resistance, **none** of the electrical energy is turned into heat, so **none** of it's
wasted. That means you can start a current flowing in a circuit using a magnetic field,
take away the magnet and the current would carry on flowing **forever**. Neat.

6) There's a catch, though. Most 'normal' conductors, e.g. metals, have transition temperatures
below **10 kelvin (−263 °C)**. Getting things that cold is **hard**, and **really expensive**.

7) Solid-state physicists all over the world are trying to develop **room-temperature superconductors**.
So far, they've managed to get some weird **metal oxide** things to superconduct at about **140 K (−133 °C)**,
which is a much easier temperature to get down to. They've still got a long way to go though.

I couldn't find a conductor, so you'll have to make do with this instead.

Uses of Superconductors

Using superconducting wires you could make:

1) **Power cables** that transmit electricity without any **loss** of power.

2) Really **strong electromagnets** that **don't** need a constant power source
(for use in medical applications and Maglev trains).

3) **Electronic circuits** that work really **fast**, because there's no resistance to slow them down.

Warm-Up Questions

Q1 What three factors does the resistance of a length of wire depend on?

Q2 What are the units for resistivity?

Q3 What happens to mercury when it's cooled to its transition temperature?

PRACTICE QUESTIONS

Exam Questions

Q1 Aluminium has a resistivity of 2.8×10^{-8} Ωm at 20 °C and a transition temperature of 1.2 K.

a) Calculate the resistance of a pure aluminium wire of length 4.00 m and diameter 1.0 mm, at 20 °C. [3 marks]

b) The wire is cooled to a temperature of 1 K. What is its resistance now? Explain your answer. [2 marks]

Q2 A student is trying to identify a piece of unknown thin metal wire using the table of resistivities
of common metals below. She measures the potential difference across and current through
different length pieces of the wire and calculates the resistance of each length of wire.

Metal	Resistivity at 20°C
Aluminium	2.82×10^{-8} Ωm
Silver	1.59×10^{-8} Ωm
Tungsten	5.6×10^{-8} Ωm

a) Explain why she must keep the temperature
of the wire constant at 20°C. [2 marks]

b) State one further measurement she must make
and suggest an appropriate measuring instrument. [2 marks]

c) State one assumption that she must make about
the wire in order to calculate the resistivity. [1 mark]

Superconductors and Johnny Depp — just too cool to resist...

*Superconducting electromagnets are used in magnetic resonance imaging (MRI) scanners in hospitals.
That way, the huge magnetic fields they need can be generated without using up a load of electricity. Great stuff...*

Electrical Energy and Power

Power and energy are pretty familiar concepts — and here they are again. Same principles, just different equations.

Power is the Rate of Transfer of Energy

Power (*P*) is **defined** as the **rate** of **transfer** of **energy**.
It's measured in **watts** (*W*), where **1 watt** is equivalent to **1 joule per second**.

or $$P = \frac{E}{t}$$

There's a really simple formula for **power** in **electrical circuits**:

$$P = VI$$

This makes sense, since:

1) **Potential difference** (*V*) is defined as the **energy transferred** per **coulomb**.
2) **Current** (*I*) is defined as the **number** of **coulombs** transferred per **second**.
3) So **p.d.** × **current** is **energy transferred per second**, i.e. **power**.

He didn't know when, he didn't know where... but one day this PEt would get his revenge.

You know from the definition of **resistance** that: $V = IR$

Combining the **two equations** gives you loads of **different** ways to **calculate power**.

$$P = VI$$ $$P = \frac{V^2}{R}$$ $$P = I^2R$$

Obviously, which equation you should use depends on what **quantities** you're given in the **question**.

Phew... that's quite a few equations to learn and love. And as if they're not exciting enough, here are some examples to get your teeth into...

Example 1: A 24 W car headlamp is connected to a 12 V car battery.
Assume the wires connecting the lamp to the battery have negligible resistance.
a) How much energy will the lamp convert into light and heat energy in 2 hours?
b) Find the total resistance of the lamp.

a) Number of seconds in 2 hours = 2 × 60 × 60 = 7200 s
$E = P \times t = 24 \times 7200 = 172\ 800$ J = **170 kJ (to 2 s.f.)**

b) Rearrange the equation $P = \frac{V^2}{R}$, $R = \frac{V^2}{P} = \frac{12^2}{24} = \frac{144}{24} = $ **6 Ω**

Example 2: A robotic mutant Santa from the future converts 750 J of electrical energy into heat every second.
a) What is the power of the robotic mutant Santa?
b) All of the robotic mutant Santa's components are connected in series, with a total resistance of 30 Ω. What current flows through his wire veins?

a) Power $= \frac{E}{t} = \frac{750}{1} = $ **750 W**

b) Rearrange the equation $P = I^2R$, $I = \sqrt{\frac{P}{R}} = \sqrt{\frac{750}{30}} = \sqrt{25} = $ **5 A**

Electrical Energy and Power

Energy is Easy to Calculate if you Know the Power

Sometimes it's the **total energy** transferred that you're interested in. In this case you simply need to **multiply** the **power** by the **time**. So:

$$E = VIt$$

(or $E = \frac{V^2}{R}t$, or $E = I^2Rt$)

You've got to make sure that the time is in seconds.

Example:

Betty pops the kettle on to make a brew.
It takes 4.5 minutes for the kettle to boil the water inside it.
A current of 4.0 A flows through the kettle's heating element once it is connected to the mains (230 V).

How much energy does the kettle's heating element transfer to the water in the time it takes to boil?

kettle heating element

230 V

Time the kettle takes to boil in seconds = 4.5 × 60 = 270 s.
You have the current, potential difference, and time taken, so use the equation $E = VIt$:

$E = 230 \times 4.0 \times 270 = 248\,400$ J = **250 kJ (to 2.s.f.)**

Warm-Up Questions

Q1 Power is measured in watts. What is 1 watt equivalent to?

Q2 What equation links power, voltage and resistance?

Q3 Write down the equation linking power, current and resistance.

PRACTICE QUESTIONS

Exam Questions

Q1 The circuit diagram for a mains-powered hair dryer is shown below.

230V

a) The heater has a power of 920 W in normal operation. Calculate the current in the heater. [1 mark]

b) The motor has a resistance of 190 Ω.
   What current will flow through the motor when the hair dryer is in use? [1 mark]

c) Show that the total power of the hair dryer in normal operation is about 1.2 kW. [2 marks]

Q2 A 12 V car battery supplies a current of 48 A for 2.0 seconds to the car's starter motor.
   The total resistance of the connecting wires is 0.01 Ω.

a) Calculate the energy transferred from the battery. [2 marks]

b) Calculate the energy wasted as heat in the wires. [2 marks]

Ultimate cosmic powers...

Whenever you get equations in this book, you know you're gonna have to learn them. Fact of life.
I used to find it helped to stick big lists of equations all over my walls in the run-up to the exams. But as that's possibly the least cool wallpaper imaginable, I don't advise inviting your friends round till after the exams...

E.m.f. and Internal Resistance

There's resistance everywhere — inside batteries, in all the wires (although it's very small) and in the components themselves. I'm assuming the resistance of the wires is zero on the next two pages, but you can't always do this.

Batteries have **Resistance**

Remember, I'm assuming that the resistance of the wires in the circuit is zero.

Resistance comes from **electrons colliding** with **atoms** and **losing energy** to other forms.

In a **battery**, **chemical energy** is used to make **electrons move**. As they move, they collide with atoms inside the battery — so batteries **must** have resistance. This is called **internal resistance**.

Internal resistance is what makes **batteries** and **cells warm up** when they're used.

Chemical reactions in the battery produce electrical energy.

Internal resistance (**r**)

Load resistance is the total resistance of all the components in the external circuit. You might see it called 'external resistance'.

Load resistance (**R**)

1) The amount of **electrical energy** the battery produces for each **coulomb** of charge is called its **electromotive force** or **e.m.f.** (ε). Be careful — e.m.f. **isn't** actually a force. It's measured in **volts**.

$$\varepsilon = \frac{E}{Q}$$

2) The **potential difference** across the **load resistance** (**R**) is the **energy transferred** when **one coulomb** of charge flows through the **load resistance**. This potential difference is called the **terminal p.d.** (**V**).

3) If there was **no internal resistance**, the **terminal p.d.** would be the **same** as the **e.m.f.** However, in **real** power supplies, there's **always some energy lost** overcoming the internal resistance.

4) The **energy wasted per coulomb** overcoming the internal resistance is called the **lost volts** (**v**).

Conservation of energy tells us:

| energy per coulomb supplied by the source | = | energy per coulomb transferred in load resistance | + | energy per coulomb wasted in internal resistance |

There are Loads of **Calculations** with **E.m.f.** and **Internal Resistance**

Examiners can ask you to do **calculations** with **e.m.f.** and **internal resistance** in loads of **different** ways. You've got to be ready for whatever they throw at you.

$$\varepsilon = V + v \qquad \varepsilon = I(R + r)$$
$$V = \varepsilon - v \qquad V = \varepsilon - Ir$$

Learn these equations for the exam. Only this one will be on your formula sheet.

These are all basically the **same equation**, just written differently. If you're given enough information you can calculate the e.m.f. (ε), terminal p.d. (**V**), lost volts (**v**), current (**I**), load resistance (**R**) or internal resistance (**r**). Which equation you should use depends on what information you've got, and what you need to calculate.

You Can Work Out the **E.m.f.** of **Multiple** Cells in **Series** or **Parallel**

For cells **in series** in a circuit, you can calculate the **total e.m.f.** of the cells by **adding** their individual e.m.f.s.

$$\varepsilon_{total} = \varepsilon_1 + \varepsilon_2 + \varepsilon_3 + \dots$$

This makes sense if you think about it, because each charge goes through each of the cells and so gains e.m.f. (electrical energy) from each one.

See p.92 for all the rules for parallel and series circuits.

For identical cells **in parallel** in a circuit, the **total e.m.f.** of the combination of cells is the **same size** as the e.m.f. of each of the individual cells.

$$\varepsilon_{total} = \varepsilon_1 = \varepsilon_2 = \varepsilon_3 + \dots$$

This is because the current will split equally between identical cells. The charge only gains e.m.f. from the cells it travels through — so the overall e.m.f. in the circuit doesn't increase.

E.m.f. and Internal Resistance

Time for an Example E.m.f. Calculation Question...

Example Three identical cells with an e.m.f. of 2.0 V and an internal resistance of 0.20 Ω are connected in parallel in the circuit shown to the right. A current of 0.90 A is flowing through the circuit. Calculate the total p.d. across the cells.

First calculate the lost volts, v, for 1 cell using $v = Ir$.

Since the current flowing through the circuit is split equally between each of the three cells, the current through one cell is $I/3$. So for 1 cell: $v = I/3 \times r = 0.90/3 \times 0.20 = 0.30 \times 0.20 = 0.06$ V

Then find the terminal p.d. across 1 cell using the equation: $V = \varepsilon - v = 2 - 0.06 = 1.94$

So the total p.d. across the cells combined = 1.94 = **1.9 V (to 2 s.f.)**

Investigate Internal Resistance and E.m.f. With This Circuit

1) **Vary** the **current** in the circuit by changing the value of the **load resistance** (**R**) using the variable resistor. **Measure** the **p.d.** (**V**) for several different values of **current** (**I**).

2) Record your data for V and I in a table, and **plot the results** in a graph of V against I.

To find the **e.m.f.** and **internal resistance** of the cell, start with the equation: $\boxed{V = \varepsilon - Ir}$

1) Rearrange to give $V = -rI + \varepsilon$

2) Since ε and **r** are constants, that's just the equation of a **straight line**:

Equation of a straight line
$y = mx + c$
gradient   y-intercept

P.d. / V

Intercept   Gradient = $\frac{\Delta Y}{\Delta X}$

ΔY

ΔX

Current / A

3) So the intercept on the vertical axis is ε.

4) And the gradient is $-r$.

Geoff didn't quite calculate the gradient correctly.

An **easier** way to **measure** the **e.m.f.** of a **power source** is by connecting a high-resistance **voltmeter** across its **terminals**. But, a **small current flows** through the **voltmeter**, so there must be some **lost volts** — this means you measure a value **very slightly less** than the **e.m.f.** (Although in practice the difference isn't usually significant.)

Warm-Up Questions

Q1 What causes internal resistance? Write down the equation linking e.m.f. and energy transferred.

Q2 What is the difference between e.m.f. and terminal p.d.?

Q3 Write the equation used to calculate the terminal p.d. of a power supply.

Exam Questions

Q1 A battery with an internal resistance of 0.80 Ω and an e.m.f. of 24 V powers a dentist's drill with resistance 4.0 Ω.

a) Calculate the current in the circuit when the drill is connected to the power supply. [2 marks]

b) Calculate the potential difference wasted overcoming the internal resistance. [1 mark]

Q2 A bulb of resistance R is powered by two cells connected in series each with internal resistance r and e.m.f. ε. Which expression represents the current flowing through each cell? [1 mark]

A $\frac{\varepsilon}{R+r}$ B $\frac{\varepsilon}{2(R+2r)}$ C $\frac{2\varepsilon}{R+2r}$ D $\frac{\varepsilon}{R+2r}$

Overcome your internal resistance for revision...

Make sure you know all your e.m.f. and internal resistance equations, they're an exam fave. A good way to get them learnt is to keep trying to get from one equation to another... pretty dull, but it definitely helps.

Conservation of Energy and Charge

There are some things in Physics that are so fundamental that you just have to accept them. Like the fact that there's loads of Maths in it. And that energy is conserved. And that Physicists get more homework than everyone else.

Charge Doesn't 'Leak Away' Anywhere — it's Conserved

1) As **charge flows** through a circuit, it **doesn't** get **used up** or **lost**.

2) This means that whatever **charge flows into** a junction will **flow out** again.

3) Since **current** is **rate of flow of charge**, it follows that whatever **current flows into** a junction is the same as the current **flowing out** of it.

Example: *CHARGE FLOWING IN 1 SECOND*

$Q_1 = 6\,C \Rightarrow I_1 = 6\,A$ ⟶ $Q_2 = 2\,C \Rightarrow I_2 = 2\,A$

$Q_3 = 4\,C \Rightarrow I_3 = 4\,A$

$I_1 = I_2 + I_3$

Kirchhoff's first law says:

| The total **current entering a junction** = the total **current leaving it.** |

Energy conservation is vital.

Energy is Conserved too

1) **Energy is conserved.** You already know that. In **electrical circuits**, **energy** is **transferred round** the circuit. Energy **transferred to** a charge is **e.m.f.**, and energy **transferred from** a charge is **potential difference**.

2) In a **closed loop**, these two quantities must be **equal** if energy is conserved (which it is).

Kirchhoff's second law says:

| The **total e.m.f.** around a **series circuit** = the **sum** of the **p.d.s** across each component. | (or $\varepsilon = \Sigma IR$ in symbols)

Exam Questions get you to Combine Resistors in Series and Parallel

A **typical exam question** will give you a **circuit** with bits of information missing, leaving you to fill in the gaps. Not the most fun... but on the plus side you get to ignore any internal resistance stuff (unless the question tells you otherwise)... hurrah. You need to remember the **following rules**:

Series Circuits:

1) **same current** at **all points** of the circuit (since there are no junctions)

2) **e.m.f. split** between **components** (by Kirchhoff's 2nd law), so:
$\varepsilon = V_1 + V_2 + V_3$

3) $V = IR$, so if I is constant:
$IR_{total} = IR_1 + IR_2 + IR_3$

4) cancelling the Is gives:

$$R_{total} = R_1 + R_2 + R_3$$

Parallel Circuits:

1) **current** is **split** at each **junction**, so: $I = I_1 + I_2 + I_3$

2) **same p.d.** across **all components** (three separate loops — within each loop the e.m.f. equals sum of individual p.d.s)

3) so, $V/R_{total} = V/R_1 + V/R_2 + V/R_3$

4) cancelling the Vs gives:

$$\frac{1}{R_{total}} = \frac{1}{R_1} + \frac{1}{R_2} + \frac{1}{R_3}$$

$\varepsilon = V$ in this case, as we're ignoring internal resistance.

...and there's an example on the next page to make sure you know what to do with all that...

Conservation of Energy and Charge

Worked Exam Question

Example:

A battery of e.m.f. 16 V and negligible internal resistance is connected in a circuit as shown:

a) Show that the group of resistors between X and Y could be replaced by a single resistor of resistance 15 Ω.

You can find the combined resistance of the 15 Ω, 20 Ω and 12 Ω resistors using:

$1/R = 1/R_1 + 1/R_2 + 1/R_3 = 1/15 + 1/20 + 1/12 = 1/5 \Rightarrow R = 5\ \Omega$

So overall resistance between X and Y can be found by $R = R_1 + R_2 = 5 + 10 = \textbf{15}\ \boldsymbol{\Omega}$

b) If $R_A = 20\ \Omega$:
   i) calculate the potential difference across R_A,

Careful — there are a few steps here. You need the p.d. across R_A, but you don't know the current through it. So start there: total resistance in circuit = 20 + 15 = 35 Ω, so current through R_A can be found using $I = V_{total}/R_{total}$: $I = 16/35$ A
then you can use $V = IR_A$ to find the p.d. across R_A: $V = 16/35 \times 20 = \textbf{9 V (to 1 s.f.)}$

   ii) calculate the current in the 15 Ω resistor.

You know the current flowing into the group of three resistors and out of it, but not through the individual branches. But you know that their combined resistance is 5 Ω (from part a) so you can work out the p.d. across the group:

$V = IR = 16/35 \times 5 = 16/7$ V

The p.d. across the whole group is the same as the p.d. across each individual resistor, so you can use this to find the current through the 15 Ω resistor:

$I = V/R = (16/7) / 15 = \textbf{0.15 A (to 2 s.f.)}$

Warm-Up Questions

Q1 State the formulas used to combine resistors in series and in parallel.

Q2 Find the current through and potential difference across each of two 5 Ω resistors when they are placed in a circuit containing a 5 V battery, and are wired: a) in series, b) in parallel.

PRACTICE QUESTIONS

Exam Question

Q1 For the circuit on the right:

a) Calculate the total effective resistance of the three resistors in this combination. [2 marks]

b) Calculate the main current, I_3. [1 mark]

c) Calculate the potential difference across the 4.0 Ω resistor. [1 mark]

d) Calculate the potential difference across the parallel pair of resistors. [1 mark]

e) Using your answer from part d), calculate the currents I_1 and I_2. [2 marks]

This is a very purple page — needs a bit of yellow I think...

V = IR is the formula you'll use most often in these questions. Make sure you know whether you're using it on the overall circuit, or just one specific component. It's amazingly easy to get muddled up — you've been warned.

The Potential Divider

I remember the days when potential dividers were pretty much the hardest thing they could throw at you.
Then along came A level Physics. Hey ho. Anyway, in context this doesn't seem too hard now, so get stuck in.

Use a **Potential Divider** to get a **Fraction** of a **Source Voltage**

1) At its simplest, a **potential divider** is a circuit with a **voltage source** and a couple of **resistors** in series.

2) The **potential difference** across the voltage source (e.g. a battery) is **split** in the **ratio** of the **resistances** (p.92).

3) So, if you had a **2 Ω** resistor and a **3 Ω** resistor, you'd get **2/5** of the p.d. across the **2 Ω** resistor and **3/5** across the **3 Ω**.

4) You can use potential dividers to supply a potential difference, V_{out}, between **zero** and the potential difference across the voltage source. This can be useful, e.g. if you need a **varying** p.d. supply or one that is at a **lower p.d.** than the voltage source.

The voltage has **dropped** by V_1 (the voltage across R_1) by the time it gets to here. The **remaining voltage** that can be supplied, e.g. to another component, is V_{out}.

In the circuit shown, R_2 has $\dfrac{R_2}{R_1 + R_2}$ of the total resistance. So: $\boxed{V_{out} = \dfrac{R_2}{R_1 + R_2} V_s}$

E.g. if $V_s = 9$ V and you want V_{out} to be 6 V, then you need:

$$\frac{R_2}{R_1 + R_2} = \frac{2}{3} \text{ which gives } R_2 = 2R_1$$

So you could have, say, $R_1 = 100\ \Omega$, $R_2 = 200\ \Omega$

5) This circuit is mainly used for **calibrating voltmeters**, which have a **very high resistance**.

6) If you put something with a **relatively low resistance** across R_2 though, you start to run into **problems**. You've **effectively** got **two resistors** in **parallel**, which will **always** have a **total** resistance **less** than R_2. That means that V_{out} will be **less** than you've calculated, and will depend on what's connected across R_2. Hrrumph.

Use a **Variable Resistor** to Vary the **Voltage**

If you replace R_1 with a **variable resistor**, you can change V_{out}. When $R_1 = 0$, $V_{out} = V_s$. As you increase R_1, V_{out} gets smaller.

Add an **LDR** or **Thermistor** for a **Light** or **Temperature Sensor**

1) A **light-dependent resistor** (LDR) has a very **high resistance** in the **dark**, but a **lower resistance** in the **light**.

Circuit symbol for an LDR:

2) An **NTC thermistor** has a **high resistance** at **low temperatures**, but a much **lower resistance** at **high temperatures** (it varies in the opposite way to a normal resistor, only much more so).

3) Either of these can be used as one of the **resistors** in a **potential divider**, giving an **output voltage** that **varies** with the **light level** or **temperature**.

The diagram shows a **sensor** used to detect **light levels**.

When light shines on the LDR its **resistance decreases**, so V_{out} increases.

You can include LDRs and thermistors in circuits that control **switches**, e.g. to turn on a light or a heating system.

If you replace the LDR with a thermistor, V_{out} will increase with temperature.

The Potential Divider

A **Potentiometer** uses a **Variable Resistor** to give a **Variable Voltage**

1) A **potentiometer** has a variable resistor replacing R_1 and R_2 of the potential divider, but it uses the **same idea** (it's even sometimes **called** a potential divider just to confuse things).

2) You move a **slider** or turn a knob to **adjust** the **relative sizes** of R_1 and R_2. That way you can vary V_{out} from **0 V** up to the source voltage.

3) This is dead handy when you want to be able to **change** a **voltage continuously**, like in the **volume control** of a stereo.

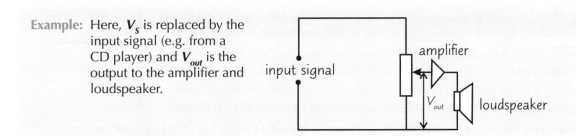

Example: Here, V_s is replaced by the input signal (e.g. from a CD player) and V_{out} is the output to the amplifier and loudspeaker.

Warm-Up Questions

Q1 Look at the light sensor circuit on page 94.
How could you change the circuit so that it could be used to detect temperature changes?

Q2 The LDR in the circuit on page 94 has a resistance of 300 Ω when in light conditions, and 900 Ω in dark conditions. The fixed resistor has a value of 100 Ω. Show that V_{out} (light) = 1.5 V and V_{out} (dark) = 0.6 V.

Exam Questions

Q1 In the circuit on the right, all the resistors have the same value.
Calculate the p.d. between:

a) A and B. [1 mark]

b) A and C. [1 mark]

c) B and C. [1 mark]

Q2 Look at the circuit on the right. All the resistances are given to 2 significant figures.

a) Calculate the p.d. between A and B as shown by a high resistance voltmeter placed between the two points. [1 mark]

b) A 40.0 Ω resistor is now placed between points A and B. Calculate the p.d. across AB and the current flowing through the 40.0 Ω resistor. [4 marks]

OI...YOU... [bang bang bang]... turn that potentiometer down...

You'll probably have to use a potentiometer in every experiment you do with electricity from now on in, so you'd better get used to them. I can't stand the things myself, but then lab and me don't mix — far too technical.

Extra Exam Practice

You've made it through <u>Section 6</u> — the last of the sections in this book. If you understood it all and answered all the questions, then it's time for some extra exam-style questions on the whole section.

- Have a look at this example of how to answer a tricky exam question.
- Then check how much you've understood from Section 6 by having a go at the questions on the next page.

---

1 A student uses the circuit in **Figure 1** in an investigation to find the resistivity of a wire at room temperature.

Figure 1

e.m.f. = 1.5 V

sample wire (A)

The student attaches different lengths of the same wire into the test circuit. He measures the length of each piece of wire and the current through the circuit. He repeats this for a range of lengths of the wire and calculates the resistance of the wire for each length. He then plots a graph of resistance against length and uses the graph to find the resistivity.

In order to keep the current through the circuit low, the battery used has a low e.m.f. and the student avoids using very short lengths of wire. The battery used has a small internal resistance which the student treats as negligible. Before the experiment, the student measures the diameter of the wire to be 0.80 mm ± 1.0%.

1.1 Explain **two** reasons why keeping the current through the circuit low will improve the results.

(4 marks)

1.2 For a length of 21.0 cm ± 0.50%, the reading on the ammeter is 0.75 A ± 0.50%. Calculate the resistivity of the wire. Include the percentage uncertainty in the resistivity. You can assume that the uncertainty in the potential difference across the wire is negligible.

(2 marks)

1.1

Think about the effects that increasing the current would have, and try to link that to the values being measured.

A low current minimises heating of the wire, which would increase the wire's resistance. Resistivity depends on resistance, $\rho = \frac{RA}{l}$, and so temperature, so the results will be more accurate if the temperature is controlled.

A low current also means that the lost volts (v) due to the internal resistance of the battery (r) are low because $v = Ir$. $V = \varepsilon - v$ so the terminal p.d. (V) can be assumed to equal the e.m.f. of 1.5 V at low currents. $R = V \div I$ so having an accurate value of V gives an accurate value for R, and hence the resistivity calculated will be more accurate.

You'd get 1 mark for saying a low current stops the wire heating up, 1 mark for saying that it keeps the terminal p.d. close to 1.5 V, and 1 mark each (up to 2) for explaining how each of these effects improve the results.

1.2

Write an equation for ρ in terms of what's been given in the question, then you can easily see which values have uncertainties.

Combine $\rho = \frac{RA}{l}$, $R = \frac{V}{I}$ and $A = \pi r^2 = \pi(\frac{d}{2})^2 = \frac{\pi d^2}{4}$

Divide the diameter by 2 to get the radius.

$\rho = \frac{V\pi d^2}{4Il} = \frac{1.5 \times \pi \times (0.80 \times 10^{-3})^2}{4 \times 0.75 \times 0.210} = 4.787... \times 10^{-6} = \mathbf{4.8 \times 10^{-6}}$ Ωm (to 2 s.f.)

The least number of significant figures given in the question is 2, so leave your final answer to 2 s.f.

$\rho = \frac{V\pi d^2}{4Il}$ so the total uncertainty is the combined uncertainty of V, I and d^2.

When raising to a power, multiply the percentage uncertainty by the power. The uncertainty in d^2 is 2 × the percentage uncertainty in d: 2 × 1.0 = 2.0%

When multiplying or dividing two or more values with uncertainties, add the uncertainties. The uncertainty in ρ is given by adding the percentage uncertainties in V, I and d^2: 0.50 + 0.50 + 2.0 = 3.0%

There's more on combining uncertainties on page 100.

So $\rho = 4.8 \times 10^{-6}$ Ωm ± 3.0% (to 2 s.f.)

You'd get 1 mark for the correct value of ρ and 1 mark for the correct uncertainty.

Extra Exam Practice

2   A student is investigating the electronic systems inside a car.

2.1   The main purpose of a car battery is to start the engine. To start the engine a very large current is supplied to the starter motor for a short amount of time. The starter motor will not start the engine unless a minimum potential difference, V, is applied across it. Most car batteries have an e.m.f. rated at approximately this minimum value, V. Explain why a car battery must have a very low internal resistance in order to start the car.

(2 marks)

2.2   Describe an experiment that the student could carry out to investigate the internal resistance of a car battery. In your answer you should include an explanation of how the student can ensure valid and accurate results.

(6 marks)

A student is designing a circuit that keeps a car's rear window glass mist-free when the temperature outside is low. **Figure 2** shows a simplified circuit that the student uses to model the five heating wires that are embedded in the glass. The heating wires get hotter the more current that flows through them. **Figure 3** shows how the resistance of the thermistor changes with the outside temperature. The resistance of resistor R_1 is 2.50 Ω.

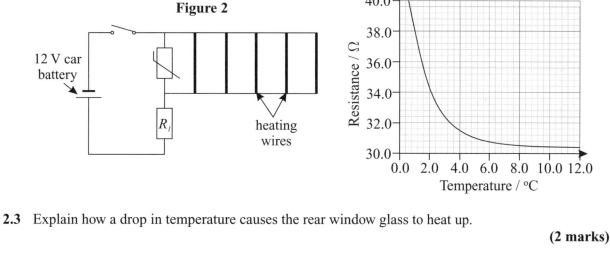

Figure 2

Figure 3

2.3   Explain how a drop in temperature causes the rear window glass to heat up.

(2 marks)

2.4   Each wire has a diameter of 0.102 mm and a length of 1.25 m. The resistivity of each wire is 3.86×10^{-8} Ωm. Show that the resistance of each of the heater wires is 5.90 Ω.

(1 mark)

2.5   Calculate the current through each heater wire when the temperature is 1.0 °C.

(3 marks)

2.6   The student designs a second circuit in which the five heating wires are attached as shown in **Figure 4**. Calculate the current through the heater wires when the outside temperature is 1.0 °C.

(2 marks)

2.7   Determine which design would heat the rear window faster at 1.0 °C.

(2 marks)

Practical and Investigative Skills

Experiment Design

Science is all about getting good evidence to test your theories... so you need to be able to spot a badly designed experiment or study a mile off, and be able to interpret the results of an experiment or study properly.
Here's a quick reference section to show you how to go about designing experiments and doing data-style questions.

Planning **Experiments** to Solve **Problems**

Scientists solve problems by **asking** questions, **suggesting** answers and then **testing** them to see if they're correct. Planning an experiment is an important part of this process to help get accurate and precise results (see p. 103).

1) Make a **prediction** — a **specific testable statement** about what will happen in the experiment, based on observation, experience or a **hypothesis** (a **suggested explanation** for a fact or observation).

2) Think about the aims of the experiment and identify the **independent**, **dependent** and other **variables**.

3) Make a **risk assessment** and plan any safety precautions.

4) Select **appropriate equipment** that will give you accurate and precise results.

5) Decide what **data** to collect and how you'll do it.

6) Write out a **clear** and **detailed method** — it should be clear enough that **anyone** could follow it and exactly repeat your experiment.

7) Carry out **tests** — to provide **evidence** that will support the prediction or refute it.

Make Sure Your Experiment is a **Fair Test**

It's important to **control** the **variables** (any quantity that can change) in an experiment. Keeping all variables **constant** apart from the independent and dependent variables, means that the experiment is a **fair test**. This means you can be more confident that any effects you see are **caused** by changing the independent variable. The variables that are kept constant (or at least monitored) in an experiment are called **control variables**.

Independent variable
The thing that you **change** in an experiment.

Dependent variable
The thing that you **measure** in an experiment.

Example: The circuit on the right is used to investigate how the current through the filament lamp varies with the voltage across it. State the independent and dependent variables in this experiment. Suggest how you would make this experiment a fair test.

Power supply.
V_s
Potentiometer (p. 95) to vary the supplied voltage
Ammeter
Filament lamp
Voltmeter

The **independent** variable will be the **voltage** across the lamp and the **dependent** variable will be the **current**.

To be a **fair test**, all the other variables must be kept the **same**. You'd use the exact same circuit throughout the experiment to make sure the length of the leads, the filament bulb and the resistance of the rest of the circuit all remained the same.

You might also use small voltages (and currents) to stop the circuit wires heating up during the experiment.

Your **Experiment** Must Be **Safe** and **Ethical**

1) You'll be expected to show that you can identify any **risks** and **hazards** in an experiment.

2) You'll need to take appropriate **safety measures** depending on the experiment. For example, anything involving **lasers** will usually need special laser **goggles** and to work with **radioactive substances** you'll probably need to wear **gloves**.

3) You need to make sure you're working **ethically** too — you've got to look after the **welfare** of any people or animals in an experiment to make sure they don't become **ill**, **stressed** or **harmed** in any way.

4) You also need to make sure you're treating the **environment ethically** too, e.g. making sure to not destroy habitats when doing **outdoor** experiments.

Monty was stressed out by the velocity experiment before it even began.

Experiment Design

Nothing is Certain

1) **Every** numerical measurement you take has an **experimental uncertainty**. The smallest uncertainty you can have in a measurement is ± **half** of one division on the measuring instrument used. E.g. using a thermometer with a scale where each division represents 2 °C, a measurement of 30 °C will at **best** be measured to be 30 ± **1 °C**.

2) The ± sign gives you the **range** in which the **true** temperature (the one you'd really like to know) probably lies — 30 ± 0.5 °C tells you the true temperature is very likely to lie in the range of 29.5 to 30.5 °C.

3) To measure a **length** with a ruler, you actually take a measurement at **each end** of the object you're measuring. There's an uncertainty in **each**. E.g. 17.0 cm measured with a mm ruler has an uncertainty of 0.05 + 0.05 = **0.1 cm**.

4) There are **two types** of error that cause experimental uncertainty:

Random errors

1) Random errors cause readings to be **spread** about the true value due to the results varying in an **unpredictable** way. They affect **precision** (see p.103).

2) They can just be down to **noise**, or measuring a **random process** such as nuclear radiation emission. No matter how hard you try, you **can't** correct them.

3) You get random error in **any** measurement. If you measured the length of a wire 20 times, the chances are you'd get a **slightly different** value each time, e.g. due to your head being in a slightly different position when reading the scale.

4) It could be that you just can't keep controlled variables **exactly** the same throughout the experiment.

Systematic errors

1) Systematic errors cause each reading to be different to the true value by the **same amount** i.e. they **shift** all of your results. They affect the **accuracy** of your results (see p.103).

2) Systematic errors are caused by the **environment**, the **apparatus** you're using, or your experimental method, e.g. using an inaccurate clock.

3) The problem is often that you **don't know** they're there. You've got to spot them first to have any chance of correcting for them.

4) If you **suspect** a systematic error, you should **repeat** the experiment with a different **technique** or **apparatus** and compare the results.

There are Loads of Ways You Can Reduce Uncertainties

1) One of the easiest things you can do is **repeat** each measurement **several times**. The **more repeats** you do, and the more **similar** the results of each repeat are, the more precise the data.

2) By taking the **mean** of repeated measurements, you will reduce the **random error** in the result. You calculate a mean by adding up all of the measurements and dividing by the total number of measurements. The **more** measurements you average over, the **less random error** you're likely to have.

3) The **smaller the uncertainty** in a result or measurement, the **smaller the range** of possible values that result could have and the more **precise** your data can be. E.g. two students each measure a length of wire three times. Student A measures the wire to be 30 cm ± 1 cm each time. Student B measures the wire to be 29 cm ± 0.5 cm each time. The **range** that student A's values could take is **larger** than student B's, so student B's data is more **precise**.

4) You should check your data for any **anomalous** results — any results that are **so different** from the **rest of the data** they cannot be explained as variations caused by random uncertainties. For example, a measurement that is ten times smaller than all of your other data values. You should not include anomalous results when you take averages.

5) You can also cut down the **uncertainty** in your measurements by using the most **appropriate** equipment. E.g. a micrometer scale has **smaller intervals** than a millimetre ruler — so by measuring a wire's diameter with a micrometer instead of the ruler, you instantly cut down the **random error** in your experiment.

6) **Computers** and **data loggers** can often be used to measure smaller intervals than you can measure by hand and reduce random errors, e.g. timing an object's fall using a light gate rather than a stop watch. You also get rid of any **human error** that might creep in while taking the measurements.

7) There's a limit to how much you can reduce the random uncertainties in your measurements, as all measuring equipment has a **resolution** — the smallest change in what's being measured that can be detected by the equipment.

8) You can **calibrate** your apparatus by measuring a **known value**. If there's a **difference** between the **measured** and **known** value, you can use this to **correct** the inaccuracy of the apparatus, and so reduce your **systematic error**. For example, to calibrate a set of **scales** you could weigh a 10.0 g mass and check that it reads 10.0 g. If these scales measure to the nearest 0.1 g, then you can only **calibrate** to within 0.05 g. Any measurements taken will have an **uncertainty** of ± 0.05 g.

9) **Calibration** can also reduce **zero errors** (caused by the apparatus **failing to read zero** when it should do, e.g. when no current is flowing through an ammeter) which can cause systematic errors.

I'm certain that I need a break...
There's a lot to take in here. Make sure you remember the different kinds of errors and how you can avoid them...

Uncertainty and Errors

Significant figures, uncertainties and error bars are all ways of saying how almost-sure you are about stuff.

Uncertainties Come in Absolute Amounts, Fractions and Percentages

Absolute uncertainty is the uncertainty of a measurement given as certain fixed quantity.
Fractional uncertainty is the uncertainty given as a **fraction** of the measurement taken.
Percentage uncertainty is the uncertainty given as a **percentage** of the measurement.

An uncertainty should also include a **level of confidence** or **probability**, to indicate how **likely** the true value is to lie in the interval. E.g. '5.0 ± 0.4 Ω at a level of confidence of 80%' means you're **80% sure** that the true value is **within** 0.4 Ω of 5.0 Ω. (Don't worry, you **don't need** to calculate the level of confidence.)

> **Example:** The resistance of a filament lamp is given as 5.0 ± 0.4 Ω. Give the absolute, fractional and percentage uncertainties for this measurement.
>
> 1) The **absolute uncertainty** is given in the question — it's **0.4 Ω**.
>
> 2) To calculate **fractional uncertainty**, divide the uncertainty by the measurement and simplify.
> The **fractional uncertainty** is $\frac{0.4}{5.0} = \frac{4}{50} = \frac{2}{25}$
>
> 3) To calculate **percentage uncertainty**, divide the uncertainty by the measurement and **multiply by 100**.
> The **percentage uncertainty** is $\frac{2}{25} \times 100 = \mathbf{8\%}$

You can **decrease** the **percentage uncertainty** in your data by taking measurements of **large** quantities. Say you take measurements with a ruler which measures to the nearest **± 0.5 mm**. The **percentage error** in measuring **10 mm** will be **± 10%**, but using the same ruler to measure a distance of **20 cm** will give a percentage error of only **± 0.5%**.

The uncertainty on a **mean** (see p.99) of repeated results is equal to **half the range** of the results.
E.g. say the repeated measurement of a current gives the results 0.5 A, 0.3 A, 0.3 A, 0.3 A and 0.4 A.
The range of these results is 0.5 − 0.3 = 0.2 A, so the uncertainty on the mean current would be **± 0.1 A**.

Sometimes You Need to Combine Uncertainties

When you do calculations involving values that have an uncertainty, you have to **combine** the uncertainties to get the **overall** uncertainty for your result.

Adding or Subtracting Data — ADD the Absolute Uncertainties

> **Example:** A wire is stretched from 4.3 ± 0.1 cm to 5.5 ± 0.1 cm. Calculate the extension of the wire.
>
> 1) First subtract the lengths without the uncertainty values: 5.5 − 4.3 = 1.2 cm
> 2) Then find the total uncertainty by adding the individual absolute uncertainties: 0.1 + 0.1 = 0.2 cm
> So, the extension of the wire is **1.2 ± 0.2 cm**.

Multiplying or Dividing Data — ADD the Percentage Uncertainties

> **Example:** A force of 15 ± 3% N is applied to a stationary object which has a mass of 6.0 ± 0.3 kg. Calculate the acceleration of the object and state the percentage uncertainty in this value.
>
> 1) First calculate the acceleration without uncertainty: $a = F \div m = 15 \div 6.0 = 2.5 \text{ ms}^{-2}$
> 2) Next, calculate the percentage uncertainty in the mass: % uncertainty in $m = \frac{0.3}{6} \times 100 = 5\%$
> 3) Add the percentage uncertainties in the force and mass values to find the total uncertainty in the acceleration: Total uncertainty = 3% + 5% = 8%
> So, the acceleration = **2.5 ms^{-2} ± 8%**

Raising to a Power — MULTIPLY the Percentage Uncertainty by the Power

> **Example:** The radius of a circle is r = 40 cm ± 2.5%. What will the percentage uncertainty be in the area of this circle, i.e. πr^2?
>
> The radius will be raised to the power of **2** to calculate the area.
> So, the percentage uncertainty will be 2.5% × 2 = **5%**

Uncertainty and Errors

Error Bars Show the Uncertainty of Individual Points

1) Most of the time, you work out the **uncertainty** in your **final** result using the uncertainty in **each measurement** you make.

2) When you're plotting a **graph**, you show the uncertainty in **each measurement** by using **error bars** to show the **range** the point is likely to lie in.

3) In exams, you might have to **analyse data** from graphs **with** and **without** error bars — so make sure you really understand what error bars are showing.

4) The **error** of **each measurement** when measuring the extension of a material is shown by the **error bars** in the graph to the right.

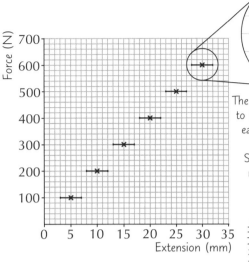

The error bars extend 2 squares to the right and to the left for each measurement, which is equivalent to 2 mm. So, the uncertainty in each measurement is ± 2 mm.

Your line of best fit (p.102) should always go through all of the error bars.

You Can Calculate the Uncertainty of Final Results from a Line of Best Fit

Normally when you draw a graph you'll want to find the **gradient** or **intercept**. For example, you can calculate k, the **spring constant** of the object being stretched, from the **gradient** of the graph on the right — here it's about 20 000 Nm⁻¹. You can find the **uncertainty** in that value by using **worst lines**:

1) Draw lines of best fit which have the **maximum** and **minimum** possible slopes for the data and which should go through all of the **error bars** (see the pink and blue lines on the right). These are the **worst lines** for your data.

2) Calculate the **worst gradient** — the gradient of the slope that is **furthest** from the gradient of the line of best fit. The blue line's gradient is about 21 000 Nm⁻¹ and the pink line's gradient is about 19 000 Nm⁻¹, so you can use either here.

3) The **uncertainty** in the gradient is given by the **difference** between the **best gradient** (of the line of best fit) and the **worst gradient** — here it's 1000 Nm⁻¹. So this is the uncertainty in the value of the spring constant. For this object, the spring constant is 20 000 ± 1000 Nm⁻¹ (or 20 000 Nm⁻¹ ± 5%).

4) Similarly, the uncertainty in the **y-intercept** is just the **difference** between the **best** and **worst** intercepts (although there's no uncertainty here since the best and worst lines both go through the origin).

When the force is O N the extension is O mm — this is a measurement with no uncertainty.

Significant Figures Can Show Uncertainty

1) You always have to assume the **largest** amount of uncertainty in data.

2) Whether you're looking at experimental results or just doing a calculation question in an exam, you must round your results to have the **same number** of significant figures as the given data value with the **least** significant figures. Otherwise you'd be saying there is less uncertainty in your result than in the data used to calculate it.

3) If no uncertainty is given for a value, the number of **significant figures** a value has gives you an estimate of the **uncertainty**. For example, 2 N only has **1 significant figure**, so without any other information you know this value must be 2 ± 0.5 N — if the value was less than 1.5 N it would have been rounded to 1 N (to 1 s.f.), if it was greater than 2.5 N it would have been rounded to 3 N (to 1 s.f.).

I'd give uncertainties 4 ± 2 for fun...

There's lots of maths to get your head around here, but just keep practising calculating uncertainties and you'll learn the rules in no time. Well... t = 0 ± 4 hours, sorry. Have another read and flip the book over, then scribble down the key points you can remember. Keep doing it until you can remember all the uncertainty joy without having to sneak a look.

Presenting and Evaluating Data

Once you've got results, you have to present them in a sensible way using a graph. Then it's time to evaluate them and use them to form a conclusion that is supported by your results.

Data can be **Discrete**, **Continuous**, **Categoric** or **Ordered**

Experiments always involve some sort of measurement to provide data.
There are different types of data — and you need to know what they are.

1) **Discrete data** — you get discrete data by **counting**. E.g. the number of weights added to the end of a spring would be discrete. You can't have 1.25 weights.

2) **Continuous data** — a continuous variable can have **any value** on a scale. For example, the extension of a spring or the current through a circuit. You can never measure the exact value of a continuous variable.

3) **Categoric data** — a categoric variable has values that can be **sorted** into **categories**. For example, types of material might be brass, wood, glass, steel.

4) **Ordered (ordinal) data** — ordered data is similar to **categoric**, but the categories can be put **in order**. For example, if you classify frequencies of light as 'low', 'fairly high' and 'very high' you'd have ordered data.

Graphs — Use the **Best Type** for the Data You've Got

You'll usually be expected to make a **graph** of your results. Not only are graphs **pretty**, they make your data **easier to understand** — so long as you choose the right type. No matter what the type though, make sure you always **label your axes** — including **units**. Choose a **sensible scale** for your axes and **plot points accurately** using a sharp pencil.

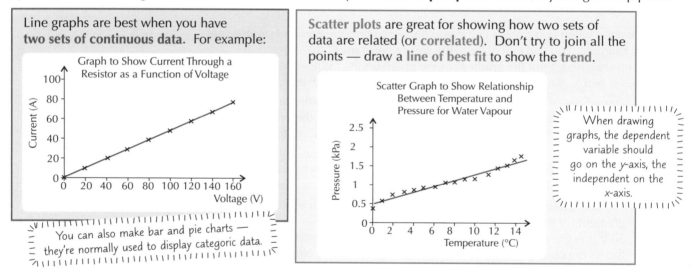

Line graphs are best when you have **two sets of continuous data**. For example:

Graph to Show Current Through a Resistor as a Function of Voltage

You can also make bar and pie charts — they're normally used to display categoric data.

Scatter plots are great for showing how two sets of data are related (or **correlated**). Don't try to join all the points — draw a **line of best fit** to show the **trend**.

Scatter Graph to Show Relationship Between Temperature and Pressure for Water Vapour

When drawing graphs, the dependent variable should go on the y-axis, the independent on the x-axis.

Correlation Shows **Trends** in Data

1) **Correlation** describes the relationship between **two variables** — usually the **independent** and **dependent** ones.

2) Data can show **positive**, **negative** or **no correlation**. An easy way to see correlation is to plot a **scatter graph** of your data. If you can, draw a **line of best fit** to help show the **trend**.

Positive correlation — as one variable increases, the other also increases.

Negative correlation — as one variable increases, the other decreases.

No correlation — there is no relationship between the variables.

Positive correlation **Negative correlation** **No correlation**

3) If you've done a **controlled** experiment in a lab and can see **correlation** in your results, you can be fairly certain there's a **causal relationship** between the **independent** and **dependent variables**. This means that a **change** in one **causes** a change in the other.

4) But in experiments or studies **outside** the lab, you can't usually control all the variables. So even if two variables are **correlated**, the change in one may not be causing the change in the other. Both changes might be caused by a **third** variable.

Presenting and Evaluating Data

Evaluating Your Data

Once an experiment's over, you have to **explain** what the data shows.
There are some key words you need to know about (and use) when evaluating data:

1) **Precision** — the smaller the amount of **spread** of your data from the **mean**, the more precise it is. Precision only depends on the amount of **random error** in your readings.

> *Precision is sometimes called reliability.*

2) **Repeatable** — **you** can **repeat** an experiment multiple times and get the **same results**.

3) **Reproducible** — if **someone else** can recreate your experiment using different equipment or methods, and gets the **same results** you do, the results are reproducible.

4) **Valid** — the **original question** is **answered**. If you don't keep all variables apart from the one you're testing **constant**, you haven't **only** tested the variable you're investigating and so the results **aren't valid**.

5) **Accurate** — the result is really close to the **true answer**.
You can only comment on how accurate a result is if you know the true value of the result.

There's normally loads of stuff to say when you're looking at data. Have a think about...

1) What **patterns** or trends, if any, the results show.

2) Whether the experiment managed to **answer** the question it set out to answer. If it did, is this a **valid** experiment and if not, why not? How **precise** was the data?

3) How close the results are to the **true value**.

4) Did the measuring instruments have enough **resolution**?

5) Any **anomalies** in the results and the possible causes of them.

6) How **large** the **uncertainties** are. If the percentage uncertainty is large, this suggests the data is not precise and a strong conclusion cannot be made.

Nora telling everyone she was 35 was a little inaccurate.

If you're asked to analyse data in the exam, look at how many marks the question is worth — the more **marks** allocated to the question in the exam, the **more detail** you have to go into.

Drawing Conclusions From Your Data

You need to make sure your conclusion is **specific** to the data you have and is **supported** by the data — don't go making any sweeping generalisations.

Your conclusion is only **valid** if it is supported by **valid data**, known as **evidence**.

Example:
> The stress of a material X was measured at strains of 0.002, 0.004, 0.006, 0.008 and 0.010. Each strain reading had an error of 0.001. All other variables were kept constant. A science magazine concluded from a graph of this data that material X's yield point is at a strain of 0.005. Explain whether or not you agree with this conclusion.

Their conclusion **could** be true — but the **data doesn't support this**. You can't tell **exactly** where the yield point is from the data because strain increases of 0.002 at a time were used. The stress at in-between strains wasn't measured — so all you know is that the yield point is somewhere **between** 0.004 and 0.006, as the stress drops between these values.

Also, the graph only gives information about this particular experiment. You can't conclude that the yield point would be in this range for **all experiments** — only this one. And you can't say for sure that doing the experiment at, say, a **different constant temperature** wouldn't give a different yield point.

The error in each reading is 0.001, which gives a **percentage uncertainty** of 50% for the lowest strain reading. This is very large and could mean the results are not valid, so no definite conclusions can be drawn from them.

Am I correlated? Well I suppose I'm pretty trendy...

Remember to evaluate the data thoroughly and when you make your conclusions, always back up your points using those evaluations. Use the checklist above to give you an idea of what to say. Suggest ways in which the experiment could be improved — there's some overlap here with how to improve uncertainties, so practising this is extra useful.

Synoptic Practice

Time to shake things up with some synoptic questions. In the exam, questions might link different parts of the course in single questions, and it's not always that easy to spot which section a question part is testing. I recommend practising with a nice big bunch of mixed questions to get the hang of it.

1   Read the passage below and answer the following questions.

A hydroelectric power station uses water to generate electricity by use of a dam in the path of a river, which creates a reservoir. The structure of a hydroelectric power station is shown in **Figure 1**. A cylindrical channel, known as a penstock, allows water to flow through the dam. The flow rate through the penstock is controlled by a control gate that

5   moves up or down to allow or restrict the water flow. The control gate has large forces acting on it from the water in the reservoir. At the end of the penstock there is a water turbine connected to an electrical generator, which converts energy from the water to electrical energy. The whole hydroelectric power system works with an efficiency η.

Figure 1

The power output, P, of the generator can be found using the following equation:

10                                    $P = \eta \rho Q g h$

Where ρ is the density of water (1000 kgm^{-3}), Q is the flow rate of the water in m^{3}s^{-1}, g is the gravitational field strength in Nkg^{-1}, and h is the height difference between the top and bottom of the penstock in m, which is equal to 22.0 m. The power station carries electricity to a small nearby town through 25.0 km of cable. The town has a minimum

15   demand of 4.50 MW. At this minimum power demand, the electricity is carried through the wires with a current of 831 A and a potential difference of 5.40 kV.

1.1 Derive the equation for the power generated by the turbine, $P = \eta \rho Q g h$ (line 10).

(4 marks)

1.2 The length of the penstock is 32.5 m and the cross-sectional area is 6.75 m^2. When water takes 9.50 s to flow from the top of the penstock to the bottom, this provides exactly enough power to meet the minimum demand of the small nearby town. Calculate the input power to the turbine that is needed to give an output power from the generator of 4.75 MW. ($g = 9.81$ Nkg^{-1})

(3 marks)

Synoptic Practice

1.3 The power cables that connect the power station to the nearby town are made of aluminium. Aluminium has a resistivity of 2.65×10^{-8} Ωm. Calculate the diameter of the cables.

(3 marks)

1.4 **Figure 2** shows part of a stress-strain graph for the material used for the control gate. The control gate has an area of 9.0 m² and a thickness of 36 cm.

Figure 2

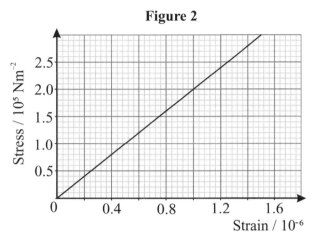

Using the graph in **Figure 2**, calculate by how much the control gate is compressed when it experiences a total force of 1.8×10^6 N from the water in the reservoir.

(2 marks)

2 Caesium-132 is an unstable element that decays by beta-plus decay.

2.1 A stationary caesium-132 nucleus decays into a xenon-132 nucleus with a mass of 2.19×10^{-25} kg. The caesium-132 emits a positron with kinetic energy 0.125 keV and an electron neutrino with momentum of 1.50×10^{-24} kgms⁻¹ in the same direction as each other. Calculate the speed of the xenon-132 nucleus. ($e = 1.60 \times 10^{-19}$ C, $m_e = 9.11 \times 10^{-31}$ kg)

(4 marks)

The positron produced during the caesium-132 decay collides with a stationary electron and they annihilate, producing two gamma ray photons as shown in **Figure 3**.

Figure 3

before   after

e^+ ⟶ e^- γ

                                         θ_1
                                         θ_2

                                         γ

The angles θ_1 and θ_2 shown in **Figure 3** are equal to each other. The wavelength of each gamma ray photon can be calculated using $\lambda = \dfrac{h}{p}$, where h is the Planck constant and p is the photon's momentum.

2.2 Explain why the two photons must have the same energy immediately after the annihilation.

(3 marks)

2.3 Calculate the frequency of one of the photons in **Figure 3**. (electron rest energy = 0.510999 MeV, $h = 6.63 \times 10^{-34}$ Js)

(2 marks)

Synoptic Practice

3   A 'solar sail' is a method of propulsion for spacecraft. A solar sail consists of a large sheet of metal foil which uses the momentum of incident photons to accelerate the spacecraft. When a photon is incident on the solar sail it is either absorbed or reflected. If the sail absorbs a photon, the photon's energy is transferred to heat energy. If a photon is reflected, it is reflected back with the same velocity as its incident velocity but in the opposite direction.

Information about two solar sails is given in **Table 1**. Each sail has the same area.

Table 1

	Sail A	Sail B
Percentage of incident photons absorbed	2%	12%
Percentage of incident photons reflected	98%	88%

3.1 The two sails in **Table 1** are attached to two different spacecraft. Explain how the acceleration of the spacecraft with sail A compares to the acceleration of the spacecraft with sail B. Assume both spacecraft have the same mass, the same number of photons hitting each sail per second, and that the incident photons strike the sail perpendicular to the surfaces of the sails.

(4 marks)

3.2 A scientist estimates that incident photons have an average momentum of 2.76×10^{-27} kgms^{-1}, and that each absorbed photon is absorbed over a time period of approximately 1.00 ms. During this time period, 1.60×10^{24} photons are incident on the surface of each sail. Estimate the total force exerted on sail B in 1.00 ms by absorbed photons.

(3 marks)

Figure 4 shows the angle to the normal of the sail, θ, at which photons strike a third sail, sail C. Sail C is attached to a spacecraft. Initially, the incident photons hit the sail at $\theta = 0°$.

Figure 4

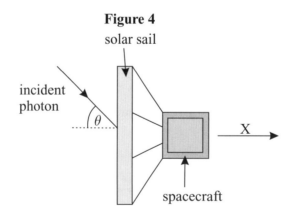

3.3 The intensity of light on the sail is the power incident on a 1 m^2 area of the sail. The intensity of light on sail C is equal to 1362 Wm^{-2}. The energy transferred in 60.0 s to sail C is 75 200 Jm^{-2}. Calculate the efficiency of sail C.

(2 marks)

3.4 When $\theta = 0°$, the force on the spacecraft in the direction of X due to incident photons is $2a$ N. The spacecraft begins to change direction causing the angle θ to increase. Calculate the angle θ at which the component of the force in the direction of X equals a N.

(1 mark)

Synoptic Practice

During use, solar sails can become positively charged, which can cause damage to the sail. The larger the positive charge, the more likely the sail is to become damaged.

3.5 The intensity of light from the Sun decreases with distance from the Sun.
Explain why a solar sail is less likely to suffer damage if it is further from the Sun.

(2 marks)

4 A baseball pitching machine is being used to bounce a baseball against the wall of a house, as shown in **Figure 5**. The baseball has a mass of 145 g.

Figure 5

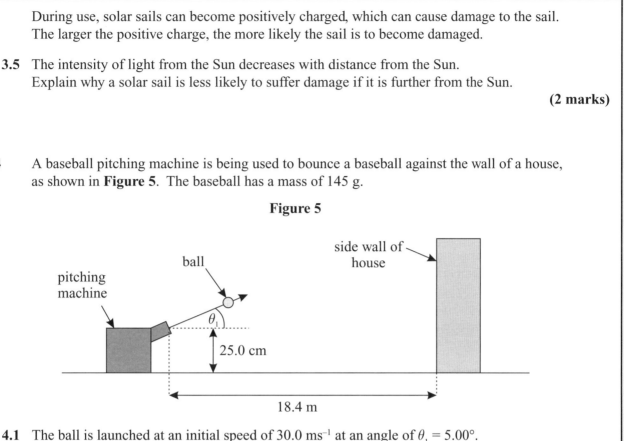

4.1 The ball is launched at an initial speed of 30.0 ms^{-1} at an angle of $\theta_1 = 5.00°$.
Calculate the velocity of the ball when it reaches the wall.
You can assume that the air resistance is negligible. ($g = 9.81$ ms^{-2})

(4 marks)

4.2 The pitching machine is adjusted so that the ball hits the wall at an angle of $\theta_2 = 35.0°$ to the normal, and bounces off the wall at an angle of $\theta_3 = 48.2°$, as shown in **Figure 6**.

Figure 6

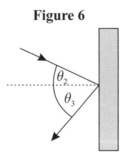

The ball hits the wall at 28.6 ms^{-1}, and the wall exerts an impulse on the ball with a horizontal component of 5.08 Ns. Calculate the final speed of the ball immediately after it has bounced off the wall.

(3 marks)

When the ball collides with the wall, it undergoes elastic deformation. The horizontal component of the force acting on the ball causes the ball to be compressed horizontally to 65% of its diameter. This horizontal deformation of the ball can be assumed to obey Hooke's law, where the baseball has a spring constant of $k = 1.03 \times 10^5$ Nm^{-1}. The ball is in contact with the wall for 1.8 ms.

4.3 Calculate the density of the baseball when it is not being compressed.

(4 marks)

Synoptic Practice

4.4 The pitching machine is adjusted again, and this time the baseball lands on the roof of the house and rolls down the roof, as shown in **Figure 7**. $h_1 = 6.50$ m and $h_2 = 5.40$ m. At its highest point on the roof, the ball is stationary. The ball leaves the roof at an angle of $\theta_4 = 32.5°$ and hits the floor 0.812 s after leaving the roof. Calculate the horizontal distance travelled by the ball between leaving the roof and reaching the floor.

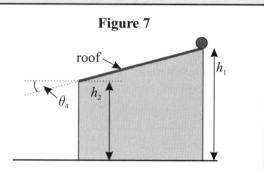

Figure 7

(3 marks)

5 An engineer designs an automatic lock for a pottery oven to ensure the oven door remains locked until the oven temperature decreases below a certain value. **Figure 8** shows the circuit used in the automatic lock. When the potential difference across the motor is large enough, it pulls the bolt upwards to remove it from the keep, unlocking the door. **Figure 9** shows how the resistance of the thermistor in the circuit changes with temperature. The circuit is powered by a battery with an internal resistance of 0.85 Ω.

Figure 8

Figure 9

5.1 Explain how the system unlocks the pottery oven as it cools.

(2 marks)

5.2 The resistance of the motor is 6.4 Ω. When the temperature of the oven is 56 °C, the total current through the circuit is 4.6 A. Calculate the e.m.f. of the battery.

(3 marks)

5.3 The spring has a spring constant of 855 Nm^{-1}. When the bolt of mass 0.540 kg is hung onto the end of the spring, the length of the spring increases. The motor pulls the bolt upwards with an acceleration of 0.142 ms^{-2} causing the spring to extend further. Calculate the total elastic strain energy stored in the spring as the bolt is accelerating. ($g = 9.81$ ms^{-2})

(3 marks)

Synoptic Practice

6   A student carries out an experiment to investigate the properties of a photocell. The circuit she uses in her experiment is shown in **Figure 10**. A photocell consists of a negatively charged photocathode and a positively charged anode separated by a small gap. When photons are incident on the photocathode, electrons can be emitted by the photoelectric effect. A potential difference between the photocathode and the anode causes the electrons to be accelerated across the gap towards the anode, creating a current flow.

In her experiment, the student shines lasers of increasing wavelengths onto the photocell and records the current read by the ammeter. Her results are shown in **Figure 11**. Each laser has the same intensity.

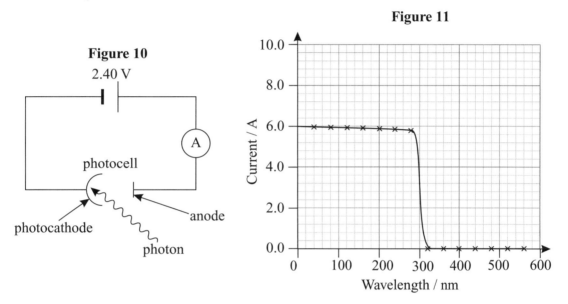

6.1   Radiation with a wavelength of 255 nm is shone onto the photocathode. The student calculates the maximum initial velocity of photoelectrons emitted from the photocathode to be 5.90×10^5 ms^{-1}. Use the results in **Figure 11** to verify the student's answer.
($h = 6.63 \times 10^{-34}$ Js, $m_e = 9.11 \times 10^{-31}$ kg, $c = 3.00 \times 10^8$ ms^{-1})

(4 marks)

6.2   Comment on the accuracy of the student's result for the maximum initial velocity of the photoelectrons, and suggest how the student could improve the accuracy of her result.

(2 marks)

6.3   Sketch a second curve on the graph to show what the curve would look like if the intensity of the lasers used in the experiment were all increased by the same amount. Label your curve 'A'.

(2 marks)

6.4   The student shines another laser on the photocell. 2.55×10^{20} photons strike the photocathode every 10.0 s. Each photon has an energy greater than the work function of the photocathode. Each incident photon releases a photoelectron, and all of the emitted photoelectrons reach the anode and contribute towards the electrical current through the circuit. Calculate the resistance of the circuit.
($e = 1.60 \times 10^{-19}$ C)

(2 marks)

6.5   The student uses one of the lasers to investigate how light behaves as a wave. She directs the laser through a diffraction grating and observes the diffraction pattern it produces. The first order maxima is at $\theta = 15.8°$. Calculate the angle of the second order diffraction maxima.

(2 marks)

Answers

Section 1 — Particles

Page 3 — Atomic Structure

1   Inside every atom there is a nucleus which contains protons and neutrons *[1 mark]*. Orbiting this core are the electrons *[1 mark]*.

2   Proton number is 8, so there are 8 protons and electrons (it's neutral) *[1 mark]*. The nucleon number is 16. This is the total number of protons and neutrons. Subtract the 8 protons and that leaves 8 neutrons *[1 mark]*.

3 a) Atoms with the same number of protons but different numbers of neutrons are called isotopes *[1 mark]*.

b) Any two from: e.g. They have the same chemical properties. / Their nuclei have different stabilities. / They have different physical properties. *[2 marks available — 1 mark for each correct answer.]*

4   A $^4_2$He nucleus has 2 protons and 2 neutrons (but no electrons) *[1 mark]*.
Charge = $2 \times 1.60 \times 10^{-19} = 3.20 \times 10^{-19}$ C *[1 mark]*
Mass = $4 \times 1.67 \times 10^{-27} = 6.68 \times 10^{-27}$ kg *[1 mark]*

Specific charge = $\dfrac{\text{charge}}{\text{mass}} = \dfrac{3.20 \times 10^{-19}}{6.68 \times 10^{-27}} = 4.790... \times 10^7$

$= \mathbf{4.79 \times 10^7}$ **C kg^{-1} (to 3 s.f.)** *[1 mark]*

The actual mass of a helium nucleus is slightly less than this due to energy being released when the nucleus was made. However, you don't need to worry about this at this level.

Page 5 — Stable and Unstable Nuclei

1 a) The strong nuclear force must be repulsive at very small nucleon separations to prevent the nucleus being crushed to a point *[1 mark]*.

b) The protons repel each other with an electrostatic force and attract each other with the nuclear strong force. The strong force is not large enough to overcome this repulsion *[1 mark]*. When two neutrons are added to the nucleus, they attract each other and the protons via the strong force. The strong force is now able to balance out the force of repulsion between the protons *[1 mark]*.

2 a) $^{226}_{88}$Ra $\rightarrow$ $^{222}_{86}$Rn $+ \, ^4_2\alpha$ *[3 marks available — 1 mark for the alpha particle, 1 mark for the proton number of radon and 1 mark for the nucleon number of radon.]*

b) $^{40}_{19}$K $\rightarrow$ $^{40}_{20}$Ca $+ \, ^{\;0}_{-1}\beta + \bar{\nu}_e$ *[4 marks available — 1 mark for the beta particle, 1 mark each for the proton number and nucleon number of calcium, 1 mark for the antineutrino.]*

Page 7 — Particles and Antiparticles

1   $e^+ + e^- \rightarrow \gamma + \gamma$ *[1 mark]* This is called annihilation *[1 mark]*

2   Energy and mass are equivalent *[1 mark]*. When two particles collide, there is a lot of energy at the point of impact. This energy is converted to mass *[1 mark]*.

3   The creation of a particle of matter also requires the creation of its antiparticle. In this case no antineutron has been produced *[1 mark]*.

4   Total energy = $2 \times 9.84 \times 10^{-14} = 1.968 \times 10^{-13}$ J *[1 mark]*

$E = hf$, so $f = \dfrac{E}{h} = \dfrac{1.968 \times 10^{-13}}{6.63 \times 10^{-34}} = 2.968... \times 10^{20}$

$= \mathbf{2.97 \times 10^{20}}$ **Hz (to 3 s.f.)** *[1 mark]*

Page 9 — Forces and Exchange Particles

1   The electrostatic force is due to the exchange of virtual photons that only exist for a very short time *[1 mark]*. The force is due to the momentum transferred to or gained from the photons as they are emitted or absorbed by a proton *[1 mark]*.

2

[1 mark for showing a W$^-$ boson being exchanged from the electron to the proton, 1 mark for showing a neutron is produced.]

Answers

This is a weak interaction *[1 mark]*.
Don't forget to put the arrows on your diagram.
Remember that the weak interaction uses W bosons, and is the only force that can change protons into neutrons or neutrons into protons.

Page 12 — Classification of Particles

1   Proton, electron and electron-antineutrino *[1 mark]*. The electron and the electron-antineutrino are leptons *[1 mark]*. Leptons are not affected by the strong interaction, so the decay can't be due to the strong interaction *[1 mark]*.
Remember that it's really just the same as beta decay.
Some books might leave out the antineutrino, so don't be misled.

2   Mesons are hadrons but the muon is a lepton *[1 mark]*. The muon is a fundamental particle but mesons are not. Mesons are built up from simpler particles *[1 mark]*. Mesons interact via the strong interaction but the muon does not *[1 mark]*.
You need to classify the muon correctly first and then say why it's different from a meson because of what it's like and what it does.

3   The correct answer is **B** *[1 mark]*.
Protons and neutrons are both baryons, which are a type of hadron. Electrons are leptons.

Page 15 — Quarks

1 a) $\pi^- = d\bar{u}$ *[1 mark]*

b) Charge of down quark = –1/3 unit.
Charge of anti-up quark = –2/3 unit.
Total charge = –1 unit *[1 mark]*

2   The weak interaction converts a down quark into an up quark plus an electron and an electron-antineutrino *[1 mark]*. The neutron (udd) becomes a proton (uud) *[1 mark]*.
The lepton number L_e is conserved in this reaction.

3   The Baryon number changes from 2 to 1, so baryon number is not conserved *[1 mark]*. The strangeness changes from 0 to 1, so strangeness is not conserved *[1 mark]*.

Section 2 — Electromagnetic Radiation and Quantum Phenomena

Page 17 — The Photoelectric Effect

1   The plate becomes positively charged *[1 mark]*.
Negative electrons in the metal absorb energy from the UV light and leave the surface *[1 mark]*.
There's one mark for saying what happens, and a second mark for saying why.

2   An electron needs to gain a certain amount of energy (the work function) before it can leave the surface of the metal *[1 mark]*. If the energy carried by each photon is less than this work function, no electrons will be emitted *[1 mark]*.

Page 19 — Energy Levels and Photon Emission

1 a) i) E (eV) = V = 12.1 eV *[1 mark]*
   ii) E (J) = E (eV) $\times (1.60 \times 10^{-19}) = 12.1 \times (1.60 \times 10^{-19})$
        $= \mathbf{1.94 \times 10^{-18}}$ **J (to 3 s.f.)** *[1 mark]*

b) i)   The movement of an electron from a lower energy level to a higher energy level by absorbing energy *[1 mark]*.
   ii) $-13.6 + 12.1 = -1.5$ eV. This corresponds to n = 3 *[1 mark]*.
   iii) n = 3 $\rightarrow$ n = 2: $-1.5 - (-3.4) = \mathbf{1.9 \text{ eV}}$ *[1 mark]*
        n = 2 $\rightarrow$ n = 1: $-3.4 - (-13.6) = 10.2$ eV = **10 eV (to 2 s.f.)** *[1 mark]*
        n = 3 $\rightarrow$ n = 1: $-1.5 - (-13.6) = 12.1 =$ **12 eV (to 2 s.f.)** *[1 mark]*

Page 21 — Wave-Particle Duality

1 a) Electromagnetic radiation can show characteristics of both a particle and a wave. *[1 mark]*

b) $\lambda = \dfrac{h}{mv}$ so $mv = \dfrac{h}{\lambda} = \dfrac{6.63 \times 10^{-34}}{590 \times 10^{-9}}$ *[1 mark]*

$= \mathbf{1.1 \times 10^{-27}}$ **kg m s^{-1} (to 2 s.f.)** *[1 mark]*

2 a) $\lambda = \dfrac{h}{mv} = \dfrac{6.63 \times 10^{-34}}{9.11 \times 10^{-31} \times 3.50 \times 10^{6}}$ *[1 mark]*

$= 2.079... \times 10^{-10} = \mathbf{2.08 \times 10^{-10}}$ **m (to 3 s.f.)** *[1 mark]*

b) Either $v = \dfrac{h}{m\lambda} = \dfrac{6.63 \times 10^{-34}}{1.67 \times 10^{-27} \times 2.079... \times 10^{-10}}$ *[1 mark]*

$= 1909.28... = \mathbf{1910\ ms^{-1}}$ **(to 3 s.f.)** *[1 mark]*

Or momentum of protons = momentum of electrons
so $m_p \times v_p = m_e \times v_e$

$v_p = v_e \times \dfrac{m_e}{m_p} = 3.50 \times 10^{6} \times \dfrac{9.11 \times 10^{-31}}{1.67 \times 10^{-27}}$ *[1 mark]*

$= 1909.28... = \mathbf{1910\ ms^{-1}}$ **(to 3 s.f.)** *[1 mark]*

c) The proton has a larger mass, so it will have a smaller speed, since the two have the same kinetic energy *[1 mark]*. Kinetic energy is proportional to the square of the speed, while momentum is proportional to the speed, so they will have different momenta *[1 mark]*. Wavelength depends on the momentum, so the wavelengths will be different *[1 mark]*. This is a really hard question. If you didn't get it right, make sure you understand the answer fully. Do the algebra if it helps.

Extra Exam Practice for Sections 1 and 2
Pages 22-23

2.1 A line spectrum shows that energy can only be absorbed and emitted from an atom in discrete amounts *[1 mark]*. Energy is absorbed and emitted by electrons moving between energy levels. The amount of energy absorbed or emitted is equal to the difference between energy levels, which means electrons in atoms can only exist in discrete energy levels *[1 mark]*.

2.2 Stopping potential is related to the kinetic energy of photoelectrons by $eV_s = E_{k(max)}$

So $hf = \phi + E_{k(max)}$ becomes $hf = \phi + eV_s$

Rearrange $eV_s = hf - \phi$ to look like $y = mx + c$

On Figure 1, $y = V$ and $x = f$

$V_s = \dfrac{h}{e}f - \dfrac{\phi}{e}$

So the y-intercept, $c = -\dfrac{\phi}{e}$ *[1 mark]*

Extend the line back to the y-axis to find the intercept:
E.g.

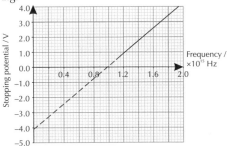

$c = -4.1$ V (accept between −4.0 and −4.2 V) *[1 mark]*
$\phi = -c \times e = 4.1 \times 1.60 \times 10^{-19} = 6.56 \times 10^{-19}$
$= \mathbf{6.6 \times 10^{-19}}$ **J (to 2 s.f.)** *[1 mark]*

2.3 The de Broglie wavelength is $\lambda = \dfrac{h}{mv}$, so for a photoelectron to have a minimum de Broglie wavelength, it must have a maximum velocity, e.g. $\lambda_{min} = \dfrac{h}{mv_{max}}$

so $v_{max} = \dfrac{h}{m\lambda_{min}} = \dfrac{6.63 \times 10^{-34}}{9.11 \times 10^{-31} \times 415 \times 10^{-12}}$

$= 1.753... \times 10^{6}$ *[1 mark]*

Photoelectrons with a velocity of v_{max} have an energy:
$E_k = \dfrac{1}{2}mv_{max}^2 = 0.5 \times 9.11 \times 10^{-31} \times (1.753... \times 10^{6})^2$
$= 1.400... \times 10^{-18}$ J *[1 mark]*

The electrons emitted from the aluminium have an initial maximum kinetic energy:
$E_{k(max)} = hf - \phi$
$= (6.63 \times 10^{-34} \times 2.10 \times 10^{15}) - (6.56 \times 10^{-19})$
$= 7.363 \times 10^{-19}$ J *[1 mark]*

The difference in energy is the kinetic energy provided by the accelerating voltage:
$1.400... \times 10^{-18} - 7.363 \times 10^{-19} = 6.645... \times 10^{-19}$ J *[1 mark]*
Convert this energy into electron volts, as 1 V provides 1 eV of energy to an electron:
$6.645... \times 10^{-19} \div 1.60 \times 10^{-19} = 4.153...$ eV
So the accelerating potential difference = **4.15 V (to 3 s.f.)** *[1 mark]*

3.1 E.g. $\bar{\nu}_e + p \rightarrow e^+ + n$ *[1 mark]*
The antineutrino must be an electron antineutrino to conserve electron lepton number *[1 mark]*. The missing particle must have a baryon number of 1 to conserve baryon number, charge is already conserved so the missing particle is neutral. A neutral particle with a baryon number of 1 is a neutron *[1 mark]*.

3.2 In annihilation, two gamma rays are produced. The total minimum energy of both the gamma rays is equal to the total rest energy of the electron and positron.
$2E_0 = 2E_{min}$ so $E_0 = E_{min} = hf_{min}$, where E_0 is the rest energy of a positron/electron.
$E_0 = 0.511 \times 10^{6} \times 1.60 \times 10^{-19}$
$= 8.176 \times 10^{-14}$ J *[1 mark]*
$E_0 = hf_{min}$ so $f_{min} = E_0 / h$
$= 8.176 \times 10^{-14} \div 6.63 \times 10^{-34}$
$= 1.233... \times 10^{20}$
$= \mathbf{1.23 \times 10^{20}}$ **Hz (to 3 s.f.)** *[1 mark]*

3.3 E.g. $c = f\lambda$ so a wave with a long wavelength has a low frequency. In order for a photoelectron to be emitted by the photoelectric effect, f has to be greater than ϕ / h *[1 mark]*. If f is too small, the photomultiplier won't emit photoelectrons when illuminated and therefore won't be able to detect any photons *[1 mark]*.

Section 3 — Waves
Page 25 — Progressive Waves

1 a) Use $c = \lambda f$ and $f = 1 / T$, so $c = \lambda / T$, giving $\lambda = cT$
$\lambda = 3.0$ ms^{-1} × 6.0 s *[1 mark]* = **18 m** *[1 mark]*
The vertical movement of the buoy is irrelevant to this part of the question.

b) The trough-to-peak distance is twice the amplitude, so the amplitude is **0.6 m** *[1 mark]*

2 $c = \lambda f$, so $f = c/\lambda = (3.00 \times 10^{8}) \div (7.1 \times 10^{-7})$
$= 4.225... \times 10^{14} = \mathbf{4.2 \times 10^{14}}$ **Hz (to 2 s.f.)** *[1 mark]*

3 **B** *[1 mark]*

Page 27 — Longitudinal and Transverse Waves

1 a) The reflected light has been partially polarised *[1 mark]*.
Only transverse waves can be polarised *[1 mark]*.

b) Polaroid material only transmits vibrations in one direction *[1 mark]*. Reflected light mostly vibrates in one direction, so Polaroid sunglasses filter out that direction, reducing glare *[1 mark]*.

2 Sound is a longitudinal wave *[1 mark]*. The vibrations are in the same direction as the energy transfer, so it cannot be polarised *[1 mark]*.

Page 29 — Superposition and Coherence

1 a) The frequencies and wavelengths of the two sources are equal *[1 mark]* and the phase difference is constant *[1 mark]*.

b) Interference will only be noticeable if the amplitudes of the two waves are approximately equal *[1 mark]*.

2 **B** *[1 mark]*
Remember, displacement and velocity are vector quantities — when two points on a wave are exactly out of phase, the phase difference is 180° and the velocity and displacement of the points are equal in size, but opposite in direction.

Page 31 — Stationary Waves

1 a) The length of the string for a stationary wave at the fundamental frequency is half the wavelength of the wave *[1 mark]*, so $\lambda = 2 \times 1.2 = $ **2.4 m** *[1 mark]*.

Answers

b) $f_{new} = \frac{1}{2l}\sqrt{\frac{2T}{\mu}} = \sqrt{2} \times \left(\frac{1}{2l}\sqrt{\frac{T}{\mu}}\right) = \sqrt{2} \times f_{original}$ **[1 mark]**

$f_{new} = \sqrt{2} \times 10$ **[1 mark]** $= 14.142...$
$= $ **14 Hz (to 2 s.f.) [1 mark]**

c) When the string forms a standing wave, its amplitude varies from a maximum at the antinodes to zero at the nodes **[1 mark]**. In a progressive wave all the points vibrate at the same amplitude **[1 mark]**.

Page 33 — Diffraction

1 For noticeable diffraction, the size of the aperture must be roughly equal to the wavelength of the wave passing through it **[1 mark]**. The size of the doorway is roughly equal to the wavelength of sound, so sound waves diffract when they pass through the gap. This allows the person to hear the fire alarm **[1 mark]**. Light has a wavelength much smaller than the size of the doorway, and so diffraction is unnoticeable. This is why the person cannot see the alarm **[1 mark]**.

2 a) E.g. Laser light is monochromatic/only contains one wavelength/ frequency of light **[1 mark]**. This provides a clearer pattern than non-monochromatic light sources as different wavelengths diffract by different amounts **[1 mark]**.

b) The central maximum will be wider and less intense **[1 mark]**. Using a narrower slit means more diffraction **[1 mark]** and so there will be fewer photons per unit area, so the intensity will be lower **[1 mark]**.

Page 35 — Two-Source Interference

1 a) Distance between sources (slit width) **[1 mark]**, spacing between two consecutive maxima or minima (fringe spacing) **[1 mark]** and the distance from the sources to the screen **[1 mark]**.

b) Any two from: Don't look into the laser beam / don't point the beam at a person / don't point the laser beam at a reflective surface / display a laser warning sign / wear laser safety goggles / turn the laser off when not in use **[1 mark for two correct suggestions]** Laser light can permanently damage your eyes/retinas **[1 mark]**.

2 a) $\lambda = c / f = 330 / 1320 = $ **0.25 m [1 mark]**

b) Separation $= w = \lambda D / s = (0.25 \times 7.3) / 1.5 = 1.21666...$
$= $ **1.2 m (to 2 s.f.) [1 mark]**

Page 37 — Diffraction Gratings

1 a) Use $d \sin \theta = n\lambda$.
For the first order, $n = 1$, so, $\sin \theta = \lambda / d$ **[1 mark]**
No need to actually work out d. The number of lines per metre is 1 / d. So you can simply multiply the wavelength by that.
$\sin \theta = 6.0 \times 10^{-7} \times 4.0 \times 10^5 = 0.24$
$\theta = \sin^{-1} (0.24) = 13.886... = $ **14° (to 2 s.f.) [1 mark]**
For the second order, $n = 2$ and $\sin \theta = 2\lambda / d$.
You already have a value for λ / d. Just double it to get sin θ for the second order.
$\sin \theta = 0.48$, $\theta = \sin^{-1} (0.48) = 28.685... = $ **29° (to 2 s.f.) [1 mark]**

b) No. Putting $n = 5$ into the equation gives a value of $\sin \theta$ of 1.2, which is impossible **[1 mark]**.

2 $d \sin \theta = n\lambda$, so for the 1st order maximum, $d \sin \theta = \lambda$
$\sin 14.2° = \lambda \times 3.7 \times 10^5$ **[1 mark]**
$\lambda = 6.629... \times 10^{-7} = $ **6.6 × 10⁻⁷ m (or 660 nm) (to 2 s.f.) [1 mark]**

Page 39 — Refractive Index

1 a) $n_{diamond} = c / c_{diamond} = (3.00 \times 10^8) / (1.24 \times 10^8) = 2.419...$
$= $ **2.42 (to 3 s.f.) [1 mark]**

b) $n_{air} \sin \theta_1 = n_{diamond} \sin \theta_2$, $n_{air} = 1$
So, $\sin \theta_1 = n_{diamond} \sin \theta_2$ **[1 mark]**
$\sin \theta_2 = \sin 50° / 2.419... = 0.316...$
$\theta_2 = \sin^{-1} (0.316...) = 18.459... = $ **18° (to 2 s.f.) [1 mark]**
You can assume the refractive index of air is 1, and don't forget to write the degree sign in your answer.

2 a) When the light is pointing steeply upwards some of it is refracted and some reflected — the beam emerging from the surface is the refracted part **[1 mark]**.

However, when the beam hits the surface at more than the critical angle (to the normal to the boundary) refraction does not occur. All the beam is totally internally reflected to light the tank, hence its brightness **[1 mark]**.

b) The critical angle is $90° - 41.25° = $ **48.75° [1 mark]**.
$\sin \theta_c = n_{air} / n_{water} = 1 / n_{water}$,
so $n_{water} = 1 / \sin \theta_c = 1 / \sin 48.75°$
$= 1.330... = $ **1.330 (to 4 s.f.) [1 mark]**
The question talks about the angle between the light beam and the floor of the aquarium. This angle is 90° minus the incident angle — measured from a normal to the surface of the water.

3 a) The cladding has a lower refractive index than the fibre, to allow total internal reflection **[1 mark]**. It also protects the cable from scratches and damage which may let light escape **[1 mark]**.

b) How to mark your answer (pick the level description that best matches your answer):
5-6 marks:
The answer fully describes several potential causes of signal degradation and correctly explains how to alter the design or operation to reduce the effects.
3-4 marks:
One potential cause of signal degradation has been fully described with a full explanation of how to reduce the effect. Another potential cause is mentioned with incomplete information or suggestions for design/operation alterations.
1-2 marks:
Potential reason(s) for signal degradation suggested but with incomplete description of the effects or of suggestions of how to reduce the effects with design changes.
0 marks:
No relevant information is given.
Here are some points your answer may include:
Absorption of light by the material the fibre is made from causes a loss of signal amplitude.
Dispersion within the fibre causes pulse broadening.
Modal dispersion is caused by light rays taking different paths of different lengths down the fibre.
Material dispersion is caused by different wavelengths of light refracting by different amounts in the fibre.
Designing the fibre so that it only allows light to take one path through it (known as a single-mode fibre) reduces pulse broadening due to modal dispersion.
Sending signals using monochromatic light reduces material dispersion because monochromatic light only has one wavelength/frequency.
Using an optical fibre repeater to boost/regenerate signals can help to reduce signal degradation over long transmission distances.

Extra Exam Practice for Section 3

Pages 40-41

2.1 The rays of light meet at the boundary.
E.g.

Since they started parallel, ray 1 must bend towards the normal more than ray 2.

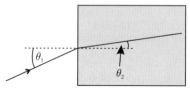

Answers

θ_2 for ray 1 must be smaller than θ_2 for ray 2 **[1 mark]**.
Snell's law is $n_1\sin\theta_1 = n_2\sin\theta_2$
n_1 = refractive index for air = 1, n_2 is the refractive index of glass = n_g
$\sin\theta_2 = \dfrac{\sin\theta_1}{n_g}$
$\sin\theta_1$ is the same for both rays of light, so the only variable affecting $\sin\theta_2$ is the refractive index. As the refractive index increases, $\sin\theta_2$ decreases. θ_2 is between 0 and 90 ° so as $\sin\theta_2$ decreases, θ_2 decreases **[1 mark]**.
The blue light has a larger n_g and therefore will have a smaller θ_2, meaning light ray 1 is the blue light **[1 mark]**.

2.2 The angle that the refracted ray makes with the glass-cladding boundary is equal to the angle of refraction:

The angle between the two rays of light (ϕ) :

$\phi = \theta_{2\text{red}} - \theta_{2\text{blue}}$ **[1 mark]**
$n_1\sin\theta_1 = n_2\sin\theta_2$, so $\theta_2 = \sin^{-1}\left(\dfrac{\sin\theta_1}{n_g}\right)$
$\theta_{2\text{red}} = \sin^{-1}\left(\dfrac{\sin 15.0}{1.513}\right) = 9.849...\ °$
$\theta_{2\text{blue}} = \sin^{-1}\left(\dfrac{\sin 15.0}{1.532}\right) = 9.726...\ °$ **[1 mark]**
$\phi = 9.849... - 9.726...$
$= 0.1233...$
$= \mathbf{0.123\ °}$ **(to 3 s.f.) [1 mark]**

2.3 Find the distance travelled by the ray of light:

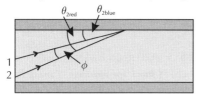

Path length of ray = 8.32×10^{-2} / cos(9.849...)
$= 0.0844...$ m **[1 mark]**
Put this value in your calculator memory for now because you'll need it again later.
The speed of red light in glass:
$n_g = c / c_g$, so $c_g = c / n_g = 3.00 \times 10^8 / 1.513$
$= 1.982... \times 10^8$ ms^{-1} **[1 mark]**
The wavelength of red light in glass:
$c_g = f\lambda$ so $\lambda = c_g / f = 1.982... \times 10^8 / 4.57 \times 10^{14}$
$= 4.338... \times 10^{-7}$ m **[1 mark]**
Number of cycles = path length / λ
$= 0.0844... / 4.338... \times 10^{-7}$
$= 194\ 628.45...$
$= \mathbf{195\ 000\ cycles}$ **(to 3 s.f.) [1 mark]**

2.4 For each ray you need to calculate the value of θ_1 when θ_c is equal to the critical angle, as shown in the diagram below:

At the critical angle, $\theta_2 = 90 - \theta_c$
$\sin\theta_1 = n_g\sin\theta_2 = n_g\sin(90 - \theta_c)$
so $\theta_1 = \sin^{-1}(n_g\sin(90 - \theta_c))$ **[1 mark]**
$\sin\theta_c = n_2 / n_1$. Here the light is moving from the glass to the cladding, so $n_1 = n_g$ and $n_2 = n_c$
so $\theta_c = \sin^{-1}(n_c / n_g)$
so $\theta_1 = \sin^{-1}(n_g\sin(90 - \sin^{-1}(n_c / n_g)))$
For red: $\theta_1 = \sin^{-1}(1.513 \times \sin(90 - \sin^{-1}(1.224 / 1.513)))$
$= 62.795...\ °$ **[1 mark]**
For blue: $\theta_1 = \sin^{-1}(1.532 \times \sin(90 - \sin^{-1}(1.231 / 1.532)))$
$= 65.777...\ °$ **[1 mark]**
The red light will be the first ray to refract into the cladding as it reaches the critical angle at a smaller angle of θ_1 than the blue light **[1 mark]**.

2.5 The blue and red lights have different frequencies/wavelengths so they are not coherent **[1 mark]**. This means that they won't produce two source interference **[1 mark]**.

2.6 The highest order fringe seen for each colour:
$n\lambda = d\sin\theta$ is a maximum when $\sin\theta = 1$
$n\lambda = d$, and $c = f\lambda$, so $n = df / c$
Red: $n = \dfrac{2.50 \times 10^{-6} \times 4.57 \times 10^{14}}{3.00 \times 10^8} = 3.808...$
So the highest order fringe that could be seen is the 3rd fringe.
Blue: $n = \dfrac{2.50 \times 10^{-6} \times 6.59 \times 10^{14}}{3.00 \times 10^8} = 5.491...$
So the highest order fringe that could be seen is the 5th fringe.
[1 mark]

2.7 The central maximum would be a purple/mixture of red and blue light **[1 mark]**. The first fringe on both sides of the central maximum would be blue. This is because $n\lambda = d\sin\theta$ and so because the wavelength for blue light is smaller, the angle of the first order diffraction will be smaller **[1 mark]**.

Section 4 — Mechanics

Page 43 — Scalars and Vectors
1 Start by drawing a diagram:

$F^2 = 20^2 + 75^2 = 6025$,
so $\mathbf{F = 78\ N}$ **(to 2 s.f.) [1 mark]**
$\tan\theta = \dfrac{20}{75} = 0.266...$
So $\boldsymbol{\theta = 15°}$ **(to 2 s.f.) to the vertical [1 mark]**.
Make sure you know which angle you're finding — and label it on your diagram. You could also answer this question by drawing a scale diagram.

2 Again, start by drawing a diagram:
Horizontal component
$v_H = 20\cos 15°$
$= \mathbf{19\ ms^{-1}}$ **(to 2 s.f.) [1 mark]**
Vertical component
$v_V = 20\sin 15° = \mathbf{5.2\ ms^{-1}}$ **(to 2 s.f.) downwards [1 mark]**
Always draw a diagram.

Page 45 — Forces
1 Weight = vertical component of tension × 2
$8 \times 9.81 = 2T\sin 50°$ **[1 mark]**
$78.48 = 0.766... \times 2T$
$102.45... = 2T$ so $\mathbf{T = 51\ N}$ **(to 2 s.f.) [1 mark]**

2 By Pythagoras:

$R = \sqrt{1200^2 + 610^2} = 1346.1...$
$= \mathbf{1300\ N}$ **(to 2 s.f.) [1 mark]**
$\tan\theta = \dfrac{610}{1200}$, so $\theta = \tan^{-1} 0.50...$
$= 26.95° = \mathbf{27°}$ **(to 2 s.f.) [1 mark]**

Page 47 — Moments
1 Moment = force × distance
$60 = 0.40F$ **[1 mark]**, so $\mathbf{F = 150\ N}$ **[1 mark]**

Answers

2 Clockwise moment = anticlockwise moment
$W \times 2.0 = T \times 0.3$
[1 mark for either line of working]
$60 \times 9.81 \times 2.0 = T \times 0.3$
$T = 3924 = $ **4000 N (to 1 s.f.)** *[1 mark]*
The moments caused by the tension in the spring
and the force exerted by the diver on the spring are equal and opposite.

Page 49 — Mass, Weight and Centre of Mass

1 a) Experiment:
Hang the object freely from a point. Hang a plumb bob from the same point, and use it to draw a vertical line down the object *[1 mark]*. Repeat for a different point and find the point of intersection *[1 mark]*. The centre of mass is halfway through the thickness of the object (by symmetry) at the point of intersection *[1 mark]*.
Identifying and reducing error: e.g.
Source: the object and/or plumb line might move slightly while you're drawing the vertical line *[1 mark]*.
Reduced by: hang the object from a third point to confirm the position of the point of intersection *[1 mark]*.

b) You can find the centre of mass of any regular shape using symmetry. The centre of mass will be at the centre where the lines of symmetry cross, halfway through its thickness *[1 mark]*.

Page 51 — Displacement-Time Graphs

1 Split graph into four sections:
A: Acceleration *[1 mark]*
B: Constant velocity *[1 mark]*
C: Stationary *[1 mark]*
D: Constant velocity in opposite direction to A and B *[1 mark]*

2 a)

[4 marks available — 1 mark for each section correctly drawn.]

b) At A: $v = \dfrac{\text{displacement}}{\text{time}} = \dfrac{5}{8} = 0.625 = $ **0.6 ms⁻¹ (to 1 s.f.)**

At B: $v = 0$

At C: $v = \dfrac{\text{displacement}}{\text{time}} = \dfrac{3}{5} = $ **0.6 ms⁻¹**

At D: $v = \dfrac{\text{displacement}}{\text{time}} = \dfrac{-8}{10} = $ **−0.8 ms⁻¹**

[2 marks for all correct or just 1 mark for 2 or 3 correct.]

Page 53 — Velocity-Time and Acceleration-Time Graphs

1 a)

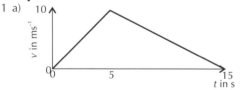

[1 mark for drawing a correctly labelled pair of axes, with a straight line between v = 0 ms⁻¹, t = 0 s and v = 10 ms⁻¹, t = 5 s. 1 mark for correctly drawing a straight line between v = 10 ms⁻¹, t = 5 s and v = 0 ms⁻¹, t = 15 s.]

[1 mark for drawing a correctly labelled pair of axes, with a straight line between a = 2 ms⁻², t = 0 s and a = 2 ms⁻², t = 5 s. 1 mark for correctly drawing a straight line from a = 2 ms⁻², t = 5 s and a = −1 ms⁻², t = 5 s, and a straight line between a = −1 ms⁻², t = 5 s and a = −1 ms⁻², t = 15 s.]

b) Distance travelled is equal to the area under v-t graph between $t = 0$ and $t = 5$ *[1 mark]* $= 0.5 \times 5 \times 10 = $ **25 m** *[1 mark]*

Page 55 — Motion With Uniform Acceleration

1 a) $a = -9.81$ ms⁻², $t = 5$ s, $u = 0$ ms⁻¹, $v = ?$
Use: $v = u + at$, $v = 0 + 5 \times -9.81$ *[1 mark]*
$v = $ **−49 ms⁻¹ (to 2 s.f.)** *[1 mark]*
NB: It's negative because she's falling downwards and we took upwards as the positive direction.

b) Use: $s = \left(\dfrac{u+v}{2}\right)t$ or $s = ut + \frac{1}{2}at^2$
$s = \dfrac{-49}{2} \times 5 = -120$ m (to 2 s.f.)
or $s = 0 + \frac{1}{2} \times -9.81 \times 5^2 = -120$ m (to 2 s.f.)
So she fell **120 m (to 2 s.f.)** *[1 mark for working, 1 mark for answer]*

2 a) $v = 0$ ms⁻¹, $t = 3.2$ s, $s = 40$ m, $u = ?$ Use: $s = \left(\dfrac{u+v}{2}\right)t$
$40 = 3.2u \div 2$ *[1 mark]*, so $u = \dfrac{80}{3.2} = $ **25 ms⁻¹** *[1 mark]*

b) E.g. use: $v^2 = u^2 + 2as$
$0 = 25^2 + 80a$ *[1 mark]*
$-80a = 625$, so $a = $ **−7.8 ms⁻² (to 2 s.f.)** *[1 mark]*

3 a) Take upstream as negative:
$v = 5$ ms⁻¹, $a = 6$ ms⁻¹, $s = 1.2$ m, $u = ?$ Use: $v^2 = u^2 + 2as$
$5^2 = u^2 + 2 \times 6 \times 1.2$ *[1 mark]*
$u^2 = 25 - 14.4 = 10.6$
$u = -3.255... = $ **−3 ms⁻¹ (to 1 s.f.)** *[1 mark]*
Take the negative root as we've defined downstream to be positive and initially the boat was travelling upstream.

b) From furthest point: $u = 0$ ms⁻¹, $a = 6$ ms⁻², $v = 5$ ms⁻¹, $s = ?$
Use: $v^2 = u^2 + 2as$
$5^2 = 0 + 2 \times 6 \times s$ *[1 mark]*
$s = 25 \div 12 = 2.083... = $ **2 m (to 1 s.f.)** *[1 mark]*

Page 57 — Acceleration Due to Gravity

1 a) The air resistance on a falling small steel ball will be less than that on a beach ball. The air resistance on the ball used in this experiment needs to be negligible in order to be able to calculate the value of *g* *[1 mark]*.

b) E.g. the ball's fall might be affected by wind *[1 mark]*. To remove this error, conduct the experiment indoors and close all windows *[1 mark]*. / Not aligning the ball and ruler at eye level can lead to a measuring error *[1 mark]*. This can be reduced by making sure your eye is perpendicular to the measuring scale being used when taking measurements *[1 mark]*.

c) E.g. there may be a delay on the stopwatch/light gates *[1 mark]*. To remove this, ensure they are properly calibrated before conducting the experiment *[1 mark]*. / The ruler may not be aligned properly so would give slightly incorrect vertical height measurements *[1 mark]*. To remove this, use a clamp to ensure the rule is straight and unmoving *[1 mark]*.

d) Use: $s = ut + \frac{1}{2}at^2$ *[1 mark]*
$u = 0$, so $s = \frac{1}{2}at^2$ or $\frac{1}{2}a = \dfrac{s}{t^2}$ *[1 mark]*
So the gradient of a graph of *s* against t^2, $\dfrac{\Delta s}{\Delta t^2}$, is equal to half the acceleration, i.e. $\frac{1}{2}g$ *[1 mark]*.

Answers

Page 59 — Projectile Motion

1 a) You only need to worry about the vertical motion of the stone.

$u = 0$ ms^{-1}, $s = -560$ m, $a = -g = -9.81$ ms^{-2}, $t = ?$

You need to find t, so use: $s = ut + \frac{1}{2}at^2$

$-560 = 0 + \frac{1}{2} \times -9.81 \times t^2$ *[1 mark]*

$t = \sqrt{\dfrac{2 \times (-560)}{-9.81}} = 10.68... = $ **11 s (to 2 s.f.)** *[1 mark]*

b) You know that in the horizontal direction:

$u = v = 20$ ms^{-1}, $t = 10.68...$ s, $a = 0$, $s = ?$

So use velocity $= \dfrac{\text{distance}}{\text{time}}$, $v = \dfrac{s}{t}$

$s = v \times t = 20 \times 10.68...$ *[1 mark]* $= $ **210 m (to 2 s.f.)** *[1 mark]*

2   You know that for the arrow's vertical motion (taking upwards as the positive direction):

$a = -9.81$ ms^{-2}, $u = 30$ ms^{-1} and the arrow will be at its highest point just before it starts falling back towards the ground, so $v = 0$ ms^{-1}.

$s = $ the vertical distance travelled from the arrow's firing point.

So use $v^2 = u^2 + 2as$. $0 = 30^2 + 2 \times -9.81 \times s$ *[1 mark]*

$900 = 2 \times 9.81s$

$s = \dfrac{900}{2 \times 9.81} = 45.87... = 45.9$ m *[1 mark]*

So the maximum distance reached from the ground

$= 45.87... + 1 = $ **47 m (to the nearest metre)** *[1 mark]*

Page 61 — Newton's Laws of Motion

1 a) Force perpendicular to river flow $= 500 - 100 = 400$ N *[1 mark]*

Force parallel to river flow $= 300$ N

Resultant force $= \sqrt{400^2 + 300^2} = $ **500 N** *[1 mark]*

b) $a = F/m$ (from $F = ma$) $= 500/250$ *[1 mark]* $= $ **2 ms^{-2}** *[1 mark]*

2   **B** *[1 mark]*

The overall acceleration is a, so ma must be equal to the resultant force, which is the force John is pushing with minus the resistance caused by friction. So $F_{John} - F = ma$, and $F_{John} = ma + F$.

3   The only force acting on each of them is their weight $= mg$ *[1 mark]*. Since $F = ma$, this gives $ma = mg$, or $a = g$ *[1 mark]*. Their acceleration doesn't depend on their mass — it's the same for both of them — so they reach the water at the same time *[1 mark]*.

Page 63 — Drag, Lift and Terminal Speed

1 a) The velocity increases at a steady rate, which means the acceleration is constant *[1 mark]*.

Constant acceleration means there must be no atmospheric resistance (atmospheric resistance would increase with velocity, leading to a decrease in acceleration). So there must be no atmosphere *[1 mark]*.

b)

[2 marks — 1 mark for drawing a graph that still starts from the origin, 1 mark for showing the graph curving to show the velocity increasing at a decreasing rate until the velocity is constant.]

Your graph must be a smooth curve which levels out. It must NOT go down at the end.

c) The graph becomes less steep because the acceleration is decreasing *[1 mark]* and because air resistance increases with speed *[1 mark]*. The graph levels out because air resistance has become equal to weight *[1 mark]*.

If the question says 'explain', you won't get marks for just describing what the graph shows — you have to say why it is that shape.

Page 65 — Momentum and Impulse

1 a) total momentum before collision = total momentum after *[1 mark]*

$(0.60 \times 5.0) + 0 = (0.60 \times -2.4) + 2v$

$3 + 1.44 = 2v$ *[1 mark]* $v = 2.22... = $ **2.2 ms^{-1} (to 2 s.f.)** *[1 mark]*

b) Kinetic energy before collision

$= \frac{1}{2} \times 0.6 \times 5^2 + \frac{1}{2} \times 2 \times 0^2 = $ **7.5 J** *[1 mark]*

Kinetic energy after the collision

$= \frac{1}{2} \times 0.6 \times 2.4^2 + \frac{1}{2} \times 2 \times 2.22^2 = 1.728 + 4.9284$

$= $ **6.7 J (to 2 s.f.)** *[1 mark]*

The kinetic energy of the two balls is greater before the collision than after (i.e. it's not conserved), so the collision must be inelastic *[1 mark]*.

2   momentum before = momentum after *[1 mark]*

$(0.7 \times 0.3) + 0 = 1.1v \Rightarrow 0.21 = 1.1v$ *[1 mark]* $\Rightarrow$

$v = $ **0.2 ms^{-1} (to 1 s.f.)** *[1 mark]*

Page 67 — Work and Power

1 a) Force in direction of travel

$= 100 \cos 40° = 76.6...$ N *[1 mark]*

$W = Fs = 76.6... \times 1500 = $

110 000 J (to 2 s.f.) *[1 mark]*

b) Use $P = Fv$

$= 100 \cos 40° \times 0.8$ *[1 mark]* $= $ **61 W (to 2 s.f.)** *[1 mark]*

2 a) Use $W = Fs$

$= 20 \times 9.81 \times 3.0$ *[1 mark]* $= $ **590 J (to 2 s.f.)** *[1 mark]*

Remember that 20 kg is not the force — it's the mass. So you need to multiply it by 9.81 Nkg^{-1} to get the weight.

b) Use $P = Fv$

$= (20 \times 9.81) \times 0.25$ *[1 mark]* $= $ **49 W (to 2 s.f.)** *[1 mark]*

Page 69 — Conservation of Energy and Efficiency

1 a) Use $E_k = \frac{1}{2}mv^2$ and $\Delta E_p = mg\Delta h$ *[1 mark]*

$\frac{1}{2}mv^2 = mg\Delta h$

$\frac{1}{2}v^2 = g\Delta h$

$v^2 = 2g\Delta h = 2 \times 9.81 \times 2.0 = 39.24$ *[1 mark]*

$v = $ **6.3 ms^{-1} (to 2 s.f.)** *[1 mark]*

'No friction' allows you to say that the change in kinetic energy is the same as the change in potential energy.

b) 2 m — no friction means the kinetic energy will all change back into potential energy, so he will rise back up to the same height as he started *[1 mark]*.

c) Put in some more energy by actively 'skating' *[1 mark]*.

2 a) If there's no air resistance, $E_k = E_p = mg\Delta h$ *[1 mark]*

$E_k = 0.02 \times 9.81 \times 8.0 = $ **1.6 J (to 2 s.f.)** *[1 mark]*

b) If the ball rebounds to 6.5 m, it has gravitational potential energy:

$E_p = mg\Delta h = 0.02 \times 9.81 \times 6.5 = 1.28$ J *[1 mark]*

So $1.57 - 1.28 = $ **0.29 J** is converted to other forms *[1 mark]*

Section 5 — Materials

Page 71 — Properties of Materials

1 a) Hooke's law says that force is proportional to extension. The force is 1.5 times as great, so the extension will be 1.5 times the original value.

Extension $= 1.5 \times 4.0$ mm $= $ **6.0 mm** *[1 mark]*

b) $F = k\Delta L$ so $k = F \div \Delta L$ *[1 mark]*

$k = 10.0 \div (4.0 \times 10^{-3}) = $ **2500 Nm^{-1}** *[1 mark]*

You could also use the values for F and ΔL from part a) to work out k.

c) Any from e.g. The string now stretches much further for small increases in force *[1 mark]*. / When the string is loosened it is longer than at the start *[1 mark]*.

2   The rubber band does not obey Hooke's law *[1 mark]* because when the force is doubled from 2.5 N to 5.0 N, the extension increases by a factor of 2.3 *[1 mark]*.

You could also work out k for both 2.5 N and 5.0 N, and show that it varies — i.e. the extension is not proportional to the force.

Page 73 — Stress and Strain

1 a) Area $= \pi r^2$ or $\pi\left(\dfrac{d}{2}\right)^2$

So area $= \pi \times \dfrac{(1.0 \times 10^{-3})^2}{4} = 7.853... \times 10^{-7}$ *[1 mark]*

Stress = force/area $= 300 \div (7.853... \times 10^{-7})$

$= $ **3.8 $\times$ 10^8 Nm^{-2} (or Pa) (to 2 s.f.)** *[1 mark]*

b) Strain = extension $\div$ length

$= (4.0 \times 10^{-3}) \div 2.00 = $ **2.0 $\times$ 10^{-3} (to 2 s.f)** *[1 mark]*

Answers

2 a) $F = k\Delta L$ and so rearranging $k = F \div \Delta L$ *[1 mark]*
   $k = 50.0 \div (3.0 \times 10^{-3}) = $ **1.7×10^4 Nm^{-1} (to 2 s.f.)** *[1 mark]*
  b) Elastic strain energy $= \frac{1}{2}F\Delta L = \frac{1}{2} \times 50.0 \times 3.0 \times 10^{-3}$
     $= $ **7.5×10^{-2} J** *[1 mark]*
     You could also use $E = \frac{1}{2}k\Delta L^2$ and substitute in your value of k.
3   The force needed to compress the spring is:
    $F = k\Delta L = 40.8 \times 0.05 = $ **2.04 N** *[1 mark]*
    The elastic strain energy in the spring is then:
    $E = \frac{1}{2}F\Delta L = \frac{1}{2} \times 2.04 \times 0.05 = $ **0.051 J** *[1 mark]*
    Assume all this energy is converted to kinetic energy in the ball.
    $E = E_{kinetic} = $ **0.051 J** *[1 mark]*.
    You could also begin by using Hooke's law to replace F in the formula for
    elastic strain energy, to give $E = \frac{1}{2}k\Delta L^2$, and then substituting into this.

Page 75 — The Young Modulus
1 Cross-sectional area $= \pi r^2$ or $\pi\left(\frac{d}{2}\right)^2$
   So area $= \pi \times \frac{(0.60 \times 10^{-3})^2}{4} = 2.827... \times 10^{-7}$ m^2 *[1 mark]*
   Stress $=$ force/area $= 80.0 \div (2.827... \times 10^{-7})$
   $= 2.829... \times 10^8$ Nm^{-2} *[1 mark]*
   Strain $=$ extension/length $= (3.6 \times 10^{-3}) \div 2.50$
   $= 1.44 \times 10^{-3}$ *[1 mark]*
   Young modulus $=$ stress/strain
   $= (2.829... \times 10^8) \div (1.44 \times 10^{-3})$
   $= $ **2.0×10^{11} Nm^{-2} (to 2 s.f.)** *[1 mark]*
2 $E = \frac{FL}{\Delta L\, A}$. Force, original length and extension are
   the same for both wires, so $E \propto \frac{1}{A}$.
   The wire B has half the cross-sectional area of the wire A. So the
   Young modulus of wire B (E_B) must be twice that of the wire A
   [1 mark].
   $E_B = 2 \times 7.0 \times 10^{10}$ Nm$^{-2} = 1.4 \times 10^{11}$ Nm^{-2}
   $= $ **1.4×10^{11} Nm^{-2} (to 2 s.f.)** *[1 mark]*
3 a) Young modulus, $E =$ stress/strain and so strain $=$ stress/E
     Strain on wire $= (2.6 \times 10^8) \div (1.3 \times 10^{11})$ *[1 mark]*
     $= $ **2.0×10^{-3} (to 2 s.f.)** *[1 mark]*
  b) Stress $=$ force/area and so area $=$ force/stress
     Area $= 100 \div (2.6 \times 10^8)$ *[1 mark]*
     $= 3.846... \times 10^{-7} = $ **3.8×10^{-7} m^2 (to 2 s.f.)** *[1 mark]*
  c) Strain energy per unit volume
     $= \frac{1}{2} \times$ stress $\times$ strain $= \frac{1}{2} \times (2.6 \times 10^8) \times (2.0 \times 10^{-3})$ *[1 mark]*
     $= $ **2.6×10^5 Jm^{-3}** *[1 mark]*
     Give the mark if answer is consistent with the value calculated for strain in
     part a).

Page 77 — Stress-Strain and Force-Extension Graphs
1 a) Liable to break suddenly without deforming plastically *[1 mark]*.
  b) E.g.

     *[1 mark for correctly-labelled axes,
     1 mark for straight line through the origin]*
2 a) Yield stress $= 900$ MNm^{-2} *[1 mark]*
  b) Tensile force $=$ stress $\times$ cross-sectional area
     $= (800 \times 10^6) \times (1.8 \times 10^{-4})$
     $= 1.44 \times 10^5$ N $= $ **1×10^5 N (to 1 s.f.)** *[1 mark]*
  c) Extension $=$ strain $\times$ unstressed length
     $= 0.2 \times 0.4 = 0.08$ m *[1 mark]*.
     Elastic strain energy $= \frac{1}{2} \times$ Force $\times$ extension
     $= \frac{1}{2} \times 1.44 \times 10^5 \times 0.08 = 5760$ J
     $= $ **6000 J (to 1 s.f.)** *[1 mark]*.

Extra Exam Practice for Sections 4 and 5

Pages 78-81
2.1 Some of the elastic strain energy (E) stored in the spring is
    converted to the kinetic energy of the pellet. Find the elastic
    strain energy when the spring is fully compressed:

$\Delta L = 4.0$ cm $= 0.040$ m, $m = 1.2$ g $= 1.2 \times 10^{-3}$ kg
Substituting $F = k\Delta L$ into $E = \frac{1}{2}F\Delta L$:
$E = \frac{1}{2}k\Delta L^2 = \frac{1}{2} \times 275 \times 0.040^2 = 0.22$ J *[1 mark]*
92% of the elastic strain energy is transferred to kinetic energy, so
$E_k = 0.92 \times 0.22 = 0.2024$ J *[1 mark]*
Rearrange $E_k = \frac{1}{2}mv^2$ to make v the subject:
$v = \sqrt{\dfrac{2E_k}{m}} = \sqrt{\dfrac{2 \times 0.2024}{1.2 \times 10^{-3}}} = 18.366...$ ms^{-1}
$= $ **18 ms^{-1} (to 2 s.f.)** *[1 mark]*

2.2 $F = \dfrac{\Delta(mv)}{\Delta t}$
    The gun and pellet are still to begin with ($v = 0$), so the total
    momentum (mv) before the pellet was fired $= 0$.
    Momentum is always conserved, so the total momentum after the
    pellet was fired $= 0$. This means that the change in momentum
    of the pellet, $\Delta(mv_{pellet})$, must equal the change in momentum of
    the gun as it recoils.
    $\Delta(mv_{pellet}) =$ pellet's final momentum $-$ pellet's initial momentum
    $= ((1.2 \times 10^{-3}) \times 18.366...) - 0$
    $= 0.02203...$ kg ms$^{-1} = \Delta(mv_{gun})$ *[1 mark]*
    Resultant force acting on the gun, $F = 4.1$ N
    $\Delta t = \dfrac{\Delta(mv)}{F} = \dfrac{0.02203...}{4.1} = 5.3756... \times 10^{-3}$ s
    $= $ **5.4×10^{-3} s (to 2 s.f.)** *[1 mark]*
    You'd still get the marks if you used 18 ms^{-1} for the initial speed of the pellet.
2.3 It's assumed that gravity is the only force acting on the pellet, so
    the pellet will move with a constant downwards acceleration, g.
    Use the equations for uniform acceleration to find t:
    Resolve vertically, taking upwards as positive:
    $s = -3.7$ m, $u = (18.366... \sin 20)$ ms^{-1}, $a = -9.81$ ms^{-2}, $t = ?$
    $s = ut + \frac{1}{2}at^2$
    $-3.7 = (18.366... \sin 20)t + \left(\frac{1}{2} \times -9.81 \times t^2\right)$
    $4.905t^2 - 6.2817...t - 3.7 = 0$ *[1 mark]*
    Use the quadratic formula to solve for t:
    $a = 4.905$, $b = -6.2817...$, $c = -3.7$
    $t = \dfrac{-b \pm \sqrt{b^2 - 4ac}}{2a}$
    $= \dfrac{6.2817... \pm \sqrt{(-6.2817...)^2 - (4 \times 4.905 \times -3.7)}}{2 \times 4.905}$ *[1 mark]*
    $= \dfrac{6.2817... \pm \sqrt{39.4605... + 72.594}}{9.81}$
    $= \dfrac{6.2817... \pm 10.58558}{9.81}$
    $t = 1.7194...$ s or $-0.4387...$ s
    $t > 0$, so $t = $ **1.7 s (to 2 s.f.)** *[1 mark]*
    You'd still get the marks if you used 18 ms^{-1} for the initial speed of the pellet.
2.4 No forces act horizontally, so the pellet maintains a constant
    horizontal velocity of $(18.366... \cos 20)$ ms$^{-1} = 17.2589...$ ms^{-1}
    throughout its flight.
    Resolve vertically, taking upwards as positive to calculate the
    vertical component of the velocity as the pellet hits the lawn:
    $u = (18.366... \sin 20)$ ms^{-1}, $v = ?$, $a = -9.81$ ms^{-2}, $t = 1.7194...$ s
    $v = u + at = 18.366... \sin 20 + (-9.81 \times 1.7194...)$
    $= -10.58558$ ms^{-1} *[1 mark]*
    So as the pellet hits the lawn:

    Horizontal velocity (v_h)
    $= 17.2589...$ ms^{-1}

    Vertical velocity (v_v)
    $= 10.58558$ ms^{-1} Speed

    Calculate the speed of the pellet using Pythagoras' theorem:
    speed $= \sqrt{v_h^2 + v_v^2} = \sqrt{17.2589...^2 + 10.58558^2}$
    $= 20.2466...$ ms$^{-1} = $ **20 ms^{-1} (to 2 s.f.)** *[1 mark]*

Calculate θ using trigonometry:

$$\tan\theta = \frac{\text{opposite}}{\text{adjacent}}$$

$$\theta = \tan^{-1}\left(\frac{10.58558}{17.2589...}\right) = 31.522...° = \textbf{32° (to 2 s.f.)} \textit{[1 mark]}$$

You'd still get the marks if you used 18 ms⁻¹ for the initial speed of the pellet and 1.7 s for the time taken for the pellet to reach the ground.

2.5 The two forces acting on the pellet during its flight are its weight and the wind.
Weight = $mg = (1.2 \times 10^{-3}) \times 9.81 = 11.772 \times 10^{-3}$ N *[1 mark]*
Find the magnitude of the resultant force using a scale drawing.
E.g. let 1 cm = 2×10^{-3} N, and convert forces to lengths:
length of weight vector = $(11.772 \times 10^{-3}) \div (2 \times 10^{-3}) = 5.886$ cm
length of wind vector = $(5.2 \times 10^{-3}) \div (2 \times 10^{-3}) = 2.6$ cm
[1 mark]

5.9 cm
(weight)

7.6 cm
(resultant)

32°

2.6 cm
(wind)

Your ruler will only be accurate to the nearest mm, so the lengths of the vectors are rounded slightly.
resultant force = $7.6 \times (2 \times 10^{-3}) = 0.0152$ N
= **0.015 N (to 2 s.f.)** *[1 mark]*

3.1 Power = work done ÷ change in time
Work done = force × distance
To find the force applied by the motor, use:
Resultant force = force applied by the motor – weight acting down the ramp – frictional force
Resultant force: $F = ma = 2.4 \times 14.6 = 35.04$ N
Weight acting down the ramp: $mg\sin\theta = 2.4 \times 9.81 \times \sin28$
$= 11.053...$ N
Frictional force: $\mu R = \mu \times mg\cos\theta = 0.81 \times 2.4 \times 9.81 \times \cos28$
$= 16.838...$ N *[1 mark]*
So now find the force applied by the motor:
$35.04 = F_{motor} - 11.053... - 16.838...$
$F_{motor} = 62.931...$ N *[1 mark]*
Work done by the motor on the box = $Fs = 62.931... \times 1.4$
$= 88.104...$ J *[1 mark]*
Motor output power = $\Delta W \div \Delta t = 88.104... \div 2.2$
$= 40.047...$ W = **40 W (to 2 s.f.)** *[1 mark]*

3.2 For the first d m, the box moves up the ramp with a constant acceleration of 14.6 ms⁻².
After this, the motor is switched off, so the resultant force acting on the box = weight acting down the ramp + friction
$= 11.053... + 16.838... = 27.891...$ N *[1 mark]*
Acceleration of the box down the ramp after it has travelled d m:
$F = ma$, so $a = F \div m = 27.891... \div 2.4 = 11.621...$ ms⁻² *[1 mark]*
Use equations for uniform acceleration to calculate the value of d:
For the first d m:
Let the direction of motion of the box be positive.
$s = d$ m, $u = 0$ ms⁻¹, $v = ?$, $a = 14.6$ ms⁻²
$v^2 = u^2 + 2as = 0^2 + (2 \times 14.6 \times d) = 29.2d$
$v = \sqrt{29.2d}$ ms⁻¹ *[1 mark]*

From the point when the motor is switched off until the box reaches the top of the ramp:
$s = (1.4 - d)$ m, $u = \sqrt{29.2d}$ ms⁻¹, $v = 0$ ms⁻¹, $a = -11.621...$ ms⁻²
$v^2 = u^2 + 2as$
$0^2 = \left(\sqrt{29.2d}\right)^2 + (2a \times (1.4-d)) \rightarrow 0 = 29.2d + 2.8a - 2ad$
$29.2d - 2ad = -2.8a \rightarrow (29.2 - 2a)d = -2.8a$
$d = \frac{-2.8a}{29.2 - 2a} = \frac{(-2.8) \times (-11.621...)}{29.2 - (2 \times (-11.621...))}$
$= 0.62048... = \textbf{0.62 m (to 2 s.f.)}$ *[1 mark]*

3.3 $F = ma$, so F and m will need to be expressed in terms of W_1, W_2 and g.
Because the box and the mass are attached, they behave as a single moving system. This means the mass of the whole system should be considered when using F = ma.
The resultant force acting on the whole system is the force(s) acting in the direction of motion minus the force(s) acting in the opposite direction of motion. The only forces acting on the system are the weights of the box and mass, so:
resultant force = $W_2 - W_1$ *[1 mark]*
$W = mg$, so $m = W \div g$
The mass of the whole system, $m = \frac{W_1 + W_2}{g}$ *[1 mark]*
$a = F \div m = (W_2 - W_1) \div \frac{W_1 + W_2}{g} = \frac{(W_2 - W_1)g}{W_1 + W_2}$ *[1 mark]*

3.4 $P = Fv$, $v = \frac{\Delta s}{\Delta t}$
efficiency = $\frac{\text{useful output power}}{\text{input power}} \times 100$
useful output power = $\frac{\text{efficiency} \times \text{input power}}{100}$
$= \frac{78 \times 5.4}{100} = 4.212$ W *[1 mark]*
Magnitude of the force applied by the motor:
$W_2 - W_1 = 26.5 - m_{box}g = 26.5 - (2.4 \times 9.81) = 2.956$ N *[1 mark]*
$v = \frac{P}{F} = \frac{4.212}{2.956} = 1.4248...$ ms⁻¹ *[1 mark]*
distance travelled = 82 cm = 0.82 m
$\Delta t = \frac{\Delta s}{v} = \frac{0.82}{1.4248...} = 0.5754...$ s = **0.58 s (to 2 s.f.)** *[1 mark]*

4.1 $W = mg$ and $\rho = \frac{m}{V}$
Circumference = $2\pi r = 9.2$ cm = 0.092 m
$r = \frac{0.092}{2\pi} = 0.01464...$ m
$V_{sphere} = \frac{4}{3}\pi r^3 = \frac{4}{3}\pi \times 0.01464...^3 = 1.3149... \times 10^{-5}$ m³ *[1 mark]*
$m_{sphere} = \rho V = (0.55 \times 10^3) \times (1.3149... \times 10^{-5})$
$= 7.2322... \times 10^{-3}$ kg *[1 mark]*
$W = mg = (7.2322... \times 10^{-3}) \times 9.81$
$= 0.07094...$ N = **0.071 N (to 2 s.f.)** *[1 mark]*

4.2 The mobile is in equilibrium. The principle of moments states that the sum of the clockwise moments will be balanced by the sum of the anticlockwise moments about the pivot.
The pivot is the point where the string is attached to the mobile.
Take moments about the point of suspension:

pivot
3.0 cm 3.0 cm
rod A   rod B
7.0 cm 5.0 cm   4.0 cm 9.0 cm

To calculate the moment of each component, use $M = Fd$, where F = weight of a component and d = distance between the pivot and the component.
Anticlockwise moments:
$M_{moon} = 0.025 \times 0.15 = 0.00375$ Nm
$M_{sphere} = 0.071 \times 0.08 = 0.00568$ Nm

Answers

The centre of mass of an object is the point at which its whole weight can be considered to act at. For uniform regular solids, the centre of mass is at the centre of the object, so the centre of mass of the cylindrical rod will occur half way along its length.

$M_{\text{rod A}} = 0.120 \times 0.09 = 0.0108$ Nm *[1 mark]*

The centre of the cube lies directly below the pivot, so it does not exert a moment.

Clockwise moments:

$M_{\text{sphere}} = 0.071 \times 0.07 = 0.00497$ Nm

$M_{\text{star}} = 0.16\, W_{\text{star}}$

$M_{\text{rod B}} = 0.150 \times 0.095 = 0.01425$ Nm *[1 mark]*

Equating clockwise and anticlockwise moments:

$0.00497 + 0.16\, W_{\text{star}} + 0.01425 = 0.00375 + 0.00568 + 0.0108$

$0.16\, W_{\text{star}} + 0.01922 = 0.02023$

$0.16\, W_{\text{star}} = 0.00101$

$W_{\text{star}} = 0.00101 \div 0.16 = 0.0063125$ N

$= \textbf{0.0063 N (to 2 s.f.)}$ *[1 mark]*

You still get full marks if you used the unrounded value of the weight of a sphere in your calculation.

4.3 The question is asking for the tensile strain $\left(\frac{\Delta L}{L}\right)$ as a percentage.

Young modulus $= \dfrac{\text{tensile stress}}{\text{tensile strain}} = 2.2 \times 10^9$ Pa

stress $= \dfrac{F}{A}$

$F =$ weight of mobile

$= (4 \times 0.071) + (2 \times 0.025) + (2 \times 0.0063125) +$
$(2 \times 0.120) + (2 \times 0.150) + 1.165$

$= 2.051625$ N *[1 mark]*

radius of string is 1.0 mm $= 1 \times 10^{-3}$ m

$A = \pi r^2 = \pi \times (1 \times 10^{-3})^2 = 3.1415... \times 10^{-6}$ m^2

stress $= \dfrac{F}{A} = \dfrac{2.051625}{3.1415... \times 10^{-6}} = 6.5305... \times 10^5$ Pa *[1 mark]*

tensile strain $= \dfrac{\text{tensile stress}}{\text{Young modulus}} = \dfrac{6.5305... \times 10^5}{2.2 \times 10^9}$

$= 2.9684... \times 10^{-4}$

As a percentage:

$(2.9684... \times 10^{-4}) \times 100 = 0.029684...\%$

$= \textbf{0.030\% (to 2 s.f.)}$ *[1 mark]*

5.1 When a mass is added to the test wire, it will cause any kinks in the wire to straighten. This gives a larger extension (ΔL) for that mass than is true. Thermal expansion of the test wire during the experiment will also cause a larger value of ΔL to be recorded for a certain mass than is true. Young modulus $= \dfrac{FL}{\Delta LA}$, so both of these would cause the calculated value of the Young modulus to be lower than the true value *[1 mark]*. To reduce the effect of kinks in the wire, 0.50 kg masses are added to both wires at the start of the experiment to straighten them both out *[1 mark]*. To reduce the effect of thermal expansion, the extension of the test wire is measured relative to an identical control wire. The test wire and control wire will both expand by the same amount, so the thermal expansion will not be included in the measurements of ΔL *[1 mark]*.

5.2 E.g. stress = force ÷ area. The force is the weight (mg) of the masses acting on the test wire minus the initial 0.50 kg mass. A mass balance could have been used to measure each mass before it is added to the test wire, so that the total weight can be calculated *[1 mark]*. A (second) micrometer could have been used to measure the diameter of the wire at several points along its length. The average diameter can then be used to calculate the cross-sectional area using $A = \pi r^2$ where r is half of the wire's diameter *[1 mark]*. Strain = extension ÷ original length. The extension of the test wire is calculated from $d - d_0$. The original length of the test wire could have been measured using a ruler after the initial 0.50 kg mass had been added *[1 mark]*.

The initial 0.50 kg mass should not be included in the calculation, as it is used to straighten out the test wire. This is also why the extension is measured relative to d_0 (when the 0.50 kg mass is attached to the test wire).

5.3 The elastic limit is the point at which the wire starts to behave plastically *[1 mark]*. The student could e.g. estimate the position of the elastic limit by removing the masses from the test wire after each mass is added. She would then need to adjust the micrometer so that the spirit level is horizontal, before comparing the micrometer reading to d_0. If the two values differ, the wire has been plastically deformed *[1 mark]*. The minimum mass required for plastic deformation to be recorded will approximate the position of the elastic limit, which can be marked on the graph *[1 mark]*.

5.4 Young modulus = tensile stress ÷ tensile strain
= gradient of a stress-strain graph

gradient $= \dfrac{\Delta y}{\Delta x} = \dfrac{130 \times 10^6}{1.1 \times 10^{-3}} = 1.1818... \times 10^{11}$ Nm^{-2}

$= \textbf{1.2} \times \textbf{10}^{11}$ **Nm^{-2} (to 2 s.f.)** *[1 mark]*

5.5 Strain $= 0.11\% = 0.11 \div 100 = 1.1 \times 10^{-3}$

This occurs at a lower tensile stress than point E, so the wire behaves elastically as it undergoes a strain of 0.11%. This means that all of the work done on the wire by the masses is stored as elastic strain energy in the wire.

Area under graph gives the elastic strain energy per unit volume.

Area up to a strain of $1.1 \times 10^{-3} = 0.5 \times (130 \times 10^6) \times (1.1 \times 10^{-3})$

$= 71\,500$ Jm^{-3} *[1 mark]*

Calculate the volume of the wire:

initial length of wire = 750 mm = 0.75 m

radius of wire = $0.40 \div 2 = 0.20$ mm $= 2.0 \times 10^{-4}$ m

cross-sectional area $= \pi r^2 = \pi \times (2.0 \times 10^{-4})^2$

$= 1.2566... \times 10^{-7}$ m^2

volume = length × cross-sectional area

$= 0.75 \times (1.2566... \times 10^{-7})$

$= 9.42477... \times 10^{-8}$ m^3 *[1 mark]*

total elastic strain energy stored in the wire:

$71\,500 \times (9.42477... \times 10^{-8}) = 0.006738...$ J

$= \textbf{0.0067 J (to 2 s.f.)}$ *[1 mark]*

Section 6 — Electricity

Page 83 — Current, Potential Difference and Resistance

1 Time in seconds = $10.0 \times 60 = 600$ s. Use the formula $I = \Delta Q / \Delta t$ which gives you $I = 4500 / 600 = \textbf{7.5 A}$ *[1 mark]*

Write down the formula first. Don't forget the unit in your answer.

2 Rearrange the formula $V = W / Q$ to give $Q = W / V$ so you get $Q = 120 / 12$ *[1 mark]* $= \textbf{10 C}$ *[1 mark]*

3 a) $R = V/I = 2/12 = 0.166... = \textbf{0.17 } \Omega$ **(to 2 s.f.)** *[1 mark]*

   b) $I = V/R = 35/0.166... = \textbf{210 A}$ *[1 mark]*

   c)

[1 mark]

Answers

Page 85 — I/V Characteristics

1 a) The graph is curved, starting steep and then levelling off as voltage/current increases *[1 mark]*.

b) As the current increases, the temperature of the filament increases *[1 mark]*. As the temperature increases, the resistance increases, so the graph gets shallower *[1 mark]*.

2 As the temperature of the thermistor increases, more charge carriers are released *[1 mark]*. More charge carriers available allows more current to flow in the circuit *[1 mark]*. So the current in the circuit can be used to monitor the temperature *[1 mark]*.

Page 87 — Resistivity and Superconductivity

1 a) Area $= \pi(d/2)^2$ and $d = 1.0 \times 10^{-3}$ m
so Area $= \pi \times (0.5 \times 10^{-3})^2 = 7.853... \times 10^{-7}$ m^2 *[1 mark]*
$R = \dfrac{\rho l}{A} = \dfrac{2.8 \times 10^{-8} \times 4.00}{7.853... \times 10^{-7}} = \mathbf{0.14\ \Omega}$ **(to 2 s.f.)**
[1 mark for correct working, 1 mark for answer and unit.]

b) Resistance will now be zero *[1 mark]*.
Because aluminium is a superconductor below its transition temperature of 1.2 K *[1 mark]*.

2 a) Resistivity varies with temperature *[1 mark]* so she must find the resistivity at 20°C in order to compare it to the resistivities in the table *[1 mark]*.

b) The diameter / cross-sectional area of the wire *[1 mark]* using a micrometer / micrometer caliper / caliper *[1 mark]*.

c) E.g. the wire is cylindrical / has a circular cross section *[1 mark]*.

Page 89 — Electrical Energy and Power

1 a) $P = VI$, so heater current $= P/V = 920/230 = \mathbf{4.0\ A}$ **(to 2 s.f.)** *[1 mark]*

b) $V = IR$, so motor current $= V/R = 230/190$
$= 1.210... = \mathbf{1.2\ A}$ **(to 2 s.f.)** *[1 mark]*

c) Motor power $= V \times I = 230 \times 1.210...= 278.4...$
$= 280$ W **(to 2 s.f.)** *[1 mark]*
Total power $=$ motor power $+$ heater power
$= 278.4... + 920 = 1198$ W
$= 1200$ W (to 2 s.f.) $= \mathbf{1.2\ kW}$ **(to 2 s.f.)** *[1 mark]*

2 a) $E = VIt = 12 \times 48 \times 2.0$ *[1 mark]* $= \mathbf{1200\ J}$ **(to 2 s.f.)** *[1 mark]*

b) Energy wasted $= I^2Rt = 48^2 \times 0.01 \times 2.0$ *[1 mark]*
$= \mathbf{46\ J}$ **(to 2 s.f.)** *[1 mark]*

Page 91 — E.m.f. and Internal Resistance

1 a) $\varepsilon = I(R + r)$ so $I = \varepsilon/(R + r) = 24/(4.0 + 0.80)$ *[1 mark]*
$= \mathbf{5.0\ A}$ **(to 2 s.f.)** *[1 mark]*

b) $v = Ir = 5.0 \times 0.80 = \mathbf{4.0\ V}$ **(to 2 s.f.)** *[1 mark]*
You could have used $\varepsilon = V + v$ and calculated V using $V = IR_{drill}$

2 C *[1 mark]*
$\varepsilon = I(R + r)$, but since there are two cells in series replace r with 2r, and ε with 2ε, then rearrange to find I.

Page 93 — Conservation of Energy and Charge

1 a) Resistance of parallel resistors:
$1/R_{parallel} = 1/6.0 + 1/3.0 = 1/2 \Rightarrow R_{parallel} = \mathbf{2.0\ \Omega}$ *[1 mark]*
Total resistance:
$R_{total} = 4.0 + R_{parallel} = 4.0 + 2.0 = \mathbf{6.0\ \Omega}$ *[1 mark]*

b) $V = I_3R_{total} \Rightarrow I_3 = V / R_{total} = 12 / 6.0 = \mathbf{2.0\ A}$ *[1 mark]*

c) $V = IR = 2.0 \times 4.0 = \mathbf{8.0\ V}$ *[1 mark]*

d) E.m.f. $=$ sum of p.d.s in circuit, so $12 = 8.0 + V_{parallel}$
$V_{parallel} = 12 - 8.0 = \mathbf{4.0\ V}$ *[1 mark]*

e) $I = V/R$, so $I_1 = 4.0 / 3.0 = \mathbf{1.3\ A}$ **(to 2 s.f.)** *[1 mark]*
$I_2 = 4.0 / 6.0 = \mathbf{0.67\ A}$ **(to 2 s.f.)** *[1 mark]*
You can check your answers by making sure that $I_3 = I_2 + I_1$.

Page 95 — The Potential Divider

1 Parallel circuit, so p.d. across both sets of resistors is 12 V.

a) There are two equal resistors in the top branch of the circuit. The p.d. between points A and B is equal to the potential difference across one of these resistors: $V_{AB} = \frac{1}{2} \times 12 = \mathbf{6.0\ V}$ *[1 mark]*

b) There are three equal resistors in the bottom branch of the circuit. The p.d. between points A and C is equal to the potential difference across two of them:
$V_{AC} = \frac{2}{3} \times 12 = \mathbf{8.0\ V}$ *[1 mark]*

c) $V_{BC} = V_{AC} - V_{AB} = 8 - 6 = \mathbf{2.0\ V}$ *[1 mark]*

2 a) $V_{AB} = 50/80 \times 12 = \mathbf{7.5\ V}$ *[1 mark]*
(ignore the 10 Ω — no current flows that way)

b) Total resistance of the parallel circuit:
$1/R_T = 1/50 + 1/(10 + 40) = 1/25 \Rightarrow R_T = 25\ \Omega$ *[1 mark]*
p.d. over the whole parallel arrangement $= 25/55 \times 12 = 5.45...$ V *[1 mark]*
p.d. across AB $= 40/50 \times 5.45...$
$= 4.36...$ V $= \mathbf{4.4\ V}$ **(to 2 s.f.)** *[1 mark]*
current through 40.0 Ω resistor $= V/R$
$= 4.36.../40.0 = \mathbf{0.11\ A}$ **(to 2 s.f.)** *[1 mark]*

Extra Exam Practice for Section 6

Pages 96-97

2.1 E.g. the terminal potential difference supplied by the battery is equal to the e.m.f generated by the battery minus the lost volts ($V = \varepsilon - v$). The lost volts are equal to the current through the battery multiplied by the internal resistance ($V = \varepsilon - Ir$) *[1 mark]*. Because the current supplied is very large, the internal resistance must be very small to avoid a large value for the lost volts/to provide a large enough terminal potential difference for the starter motor to start the engine *[1 mark]*.

2.2 *5-6 marks:*
The answer describes the full experimental procedure including correct suggestions of how to ensure the results are valid and accurate, and includes explanations of why the validity/accuracy is improved. The answer may include a diagram, but this is not essential. The answer has a clear and logical structure. The information given is relevant and detailed.
3-4 marks:
The answer describes most of the experimental procedure with some briefly explained suggestions of how to improve the accuracy or validity of the results. The answer may include a diagram, but this is not essential. The answer has some structure. Most of the information given is relevant and there is some detail involved.
1-2 marks:
A few simple steps for the experiment are described. The answer may not include ways to ensure the results are accurate or valid, or may give one or two simple suggestions without detail or explanation. The answer has no clear structure. The information given is basic and lacking in detail. It may not all be relevant.
0 marks:
No relevant information is given.
Here are some points your answer may include:
The student should connect the battery to a variable resistor, with a voltmeter connected in parallel with the battery and an ammeter in series with the battery.
E.g.

The variable resistor should be adjusted to vary the current through the circuit.
For each value of current, the potential difference across the battery should be measured.
A graph of p.d. (V) against current (I) should be plotted.
$\varepsilon = V - Ir$ so rearrange this to look like $y = mx + c$. V is on the y-axis and I is on the x-axis so $V = -rI + \varepsilon$, so the gradient of the graph is equal to $-r$.

Answers

To achieve valid results, make sure only the relationship between current and p.d. is being tested / make sure that the current and the p.d. are the only variables that change / make sure all other variables are controlled.

In order for the resistance of the circuit to remain constant, the temperature of the circuit must remain constant.

Keep the temperature of the room constant.

Turn off the circuit between readings to reduce the heating of the circuit.

Use low currents to minimise heating.

Valid results must be precise. To ensure the results are precise, use a voltmeter and ammeter with small intervals on their scales. This reduces the uncertainty in readings, making them more precise.

Take multiple readings of the p.d. and calculate the mean to reduce the effect of random errors to improve the precision.

To achieve accurate results, calibrate equipment to avoid systematic errors.

2.3 When the temperature decreases, the resistance of the thermistor increases. This means that the thermistor's share of the total potential difference increases, so the potential difference across the heating wires increases *[1 mark]*. As $V = IR$, an increase in potential difference will increase the current though the wires, which will cause the wires to heat up and heat up the glass *[1 mark]*.

2.4 $\rho = \dfrac{RA}{l}$, so $R = \dfrac{\rho l}{A}$. And $A = \pi r^2$ where $r = d \div 2$.

$R = \dfrac{\rho l}{\pi (d \div 2)^2} = \dfrac{3.86 \times 10^{-8} \times 1.25}{\pi (0.102 \times 10^{-3} \div 2)^2}$

$\qquad = 5.904... = \mathbf{5.90\ \Omega}$ **(to 3 s.f.)** *[1 mark]*

2.5 $R = V / I$ so $I = V / R$. To calculate the current through each wire, first calculate the potential difference across each wire. The potential difference across each wire is equal to the potential difference across the thermistor, because they are in parallel.

The potential difference across the thermistor is $V = \dfrac{R_2}{R_1 + R_2} \times V_s$

where R_2 is the combined resistance of the thermistor and the wires. $R_{\text{thermistor}}$ is 38.0 Ω at 1.0 °C.

$\dfrac{1}{R_2} = \dfrac{1}{R_{\text{thermistor}}} + \dfrac{5}{R_{\text{wire}}} = \dfrac{1}{38.0} + \dfrac{5}{5.904...} = 0.873...$

$R_2 = 1 \div 0.873... = 1.145...\ \Omega$ *[1 mark]*

$V = \dfrac{R_2}{R_1 + R_2} \times V_s = \dfrac{1.145...}{2.50 + 1.145...} \times 12 = 3.770...\ \text{V}$ *[1 mark]*

$I = \dfrac{V}{R_{\text{wire}}} = \dfrac{3.770...}{5.904...} = 0.638... = \mathbf{0.64\ A}$ **(to 2 s.f.)** *[1 mark]*

You could have used the rounded value of R_{wire} = 5.90 Ω in your calculations here as it was given to you in question 2.4.

2.6 The wires are in series with each other, so the total resistance of the wires is $5 \times R_{\text{wire}}$.

The wires are in parallel with the thermistor, so the total resistance of the wires and thermistor, R_2 is given by:

$\dfrac{1}{R_2} = \dfrac{1}{R_{\text{thermistor}}} + \dfrac{1}{5 \times R_{\text{wire}}} = \dfrac{1}{38.0} + \dfrac{1}{5 \times 5.904...} = 0.0601...$

$R_2 = 1 \div 0.0601... = 16.615...\ \Omega$ *[1 mark]*

$V = \dfrac{R_2}{R_1 + R_2} \times V_s = \dfrac{16.615...}{2.50 + 16.615...} \times 12 = 10.430...\ \text{V}$

$I = \dfrac{V}{R}$ where R is the total resistance of the 5 wires:

$I = \dfrac{V}{5 \times R_{\text{wire}}} = \dfrac{10.430...}{5 \times 5.904...} = 0.353... = \mathbf{0.35\ A}$ **(to 2 s.f.)** *[1 mark]*

You could have used the rounded value of R_{wire} = 5.90 Ω in your calculations here as it was given to you in question 2.4.

2.7 The amount of heating depends on the energy transferred in a certain time/the power.

Figure 2: $P = VI = 3.8 \times 0.64 = 2.4$ W (to 2 s.f.)

The values for V and I here were calculated in the answer to 2.5.

Figure 4: in series, the potential difference is shared between the wires, so each wire will get $\frac{1}{5}$ of the potential difference.

$P = VI = (10 \div 5) \times 0.35 = 0.70$ W (to 2 s.f.) *[1 mark]*

The values for V and I here were calculated in the answer to 2.6.

The power dissipated by the wires in Figure 2 is larger than the power dissipated by the wires in Figure 4, so Figure 2 will heat the rear window faster *[1 mark]*.

You should normally use unrounded values in your calculations. However the rounded values can be used here as the question only asks you to find which setup dissipates the most power, rather than asking for a specific value. If instead you have correctly used your unrounded values in your calculations, then you still get a mark for your calculations and a mark for a correct conclusion.

Synoptic Practice

Pages 104-109

1.1 $P = \dfrac{\Delta W}{\Delta t}$ where ΔW is the energy transferred, so $P = \dfrac{E}{t}$.

The energy transferred to the turbine is the gravitational potential energy lost by the water:

$\Delta E_p = mg\Delta h$ so $P = \dfrac{mgh}{t}$ *[1 mark]*

$\rho = m \div V$ which is the density of the water in the penstock,

so $m = \rho V$, so $P = \dfrac{\rho V g h}{t}$ *[1 mark]*

Flow rate $= Q = V \div t$ (the units are in m³s⁻¹ which shows that it is the volume of water flowing per unit time)

$P = \rho Q g h$ *[1 mark]*

This is the total power of the water through the penstock. This power is converted to electrical energy with an efficiency of η. So the power generated is the total power $\times\ \eta$ *[1 mark]*:

$P = \eta \rho Q g h$

1.2 efficiency $= \eta = \dfrac{P}{\rho Q g h}$, so first calculate Q.

The flow rate, Q:

$Q = V \div t = (32.5 \times 6.75) \div 9.50 = 23.092...$ m³s⁻¹ *[1 mark]*

Calculate the efficiency using the minimum power demand of the small town: $\eta = \dfrac{P}{\rho Q g h} = \dfrac{4.50 \times 10^6}{1000 \times 23.092... \times 9.81 \times 22.0}$

$\qquad = 0.9029...$ *[1 mark]*

efficiency, $\eta = \dfrac{\text{useful output power}}{\text{input power}}$

so input power $= \dfrac{\text{useful output power}}{\eta}$

So when the output power equals 4.75 MW, the input power is:

$\dfrac{4.75 \times 10^6}{0.9029...} = 5.260... \times 10^6 = \mathbf{5.26 \times 10^6\ W}$ **(to 3 s.f.)** *[1 mark]*

1.3 $R = \dfrac{V}{I} = \dfrac{5.40 \times 10^3}{831} = 6.498...\ \Omega$ *[1 mark]*

$\rho = RA / L$ so $A = \rho L / R = (2.65 \times 10^{-8} \times 25.0 \times 10^3) / 6.498...$

$\qquad = 1.019... \times 10^{-4}$ m² *[1 mark]*

$A = \pi r^2$ so $r = \sqrt{\dfrac{A}{\pi}} = \sqrt{\dfrac{1.019... \times 10^{-4}}{\pi}} = 5.696... \times 10^{-3}$ m

diameter $=$ radius $\times\ 2 = 5.696... \times 10^{-3} \times 2$

$\qquad = 1.139... \times 10^{-2} = \mathbf{1.14 \times 10^{-2}\ m}$ **(to 3 s.f.)** *[1 mark]*

1.4 Young modulus $= \dfrac{\text{tensile stress}}{\text{tensile strain}} = \dfrac{FL}{A\Delta L}$

This rearranges to give $\Delta L = \dfrac{FL}{A \times \text{gradient}}$ where ΔL is the amount by which the gate will be compressed.

Young modulus = gradient of stress-strain graph, e.g.:

gradient $= \dfrac{\Delta y}{\Delta x} = \dfrac{(2.4 \times 10^5) - 0}{(1.2 \times 10^{-6}) - 0} = 2 \times 10^{11}$ Nm⁻² *[1 mark]*

$\Delta L = \dfrac{FL}{A \times \text{gradient}} = \dfrac{1.8 \times 10^6 \times (36 \div 100)}{9.0 \times 2 \times 10^{11}}$

$\qquad = \mathbf{3.6 \times 10^{-7}\ m}$ *[1 mark]*

Answers

2.1 The momentum before the decay is zero because the caesium nucleus is initially stationary. The momentum after the decay is the total momentum of the xenon nucleus, positron and neutrino. Momentum, $p = mv$, is conserved so:

$0 = p_{xenon} + p_e + p_\nu$ so $p_{xenon} = -p_e - p_\nu$

To find the positron's momentum first calculate its velocity:

E_k in joules $= 0.125 \times 10^3 \times 1.60 \times 10^{-19} = 2 \times 10^{-17}$ J

$E_k = \frac{1}{2}mv^2$ so $v = \sqrt{\dfrac{2E_k}{m_e}} = \sqrt{\dfrac{2 \times 2 \times 10^{-17}}{9.11 \times 10^{-31}}}$
$= 6.626... \times 10^6$ ms^{-1} *[1 mark]*

The mass of a positron is the same as the mass of an electron as it is the electron's antiparticle.

Positron momentum: $p_e = m_e v_e = 9.11 \times 10^{-31} \times 6.626... \times 10^6$
$= 6.036... \times 10^{-24}$ kgms^{-1} *[1 mark]*

$p_{xenon} = -p_e - p_\nu = (-6.036... \times 10^{-24}) - (1.50 \times 10^{-24})$
$= -7.536... \times 10^{-24}$ kgms^{-1} *[1 mark]*

$p_{xenon} = m_{xenon}v_{xenon}$

so $v_{xenon} = p_{xenon} / m_{xenon} = (-7.536... \times 10^{-24}) / (2.19 \times 10^{-25})$
$= -34.413...$
$= $ **34.4 ms^{-1} (to 3 s.f.)** *[1 mark]*

You can ignore the minus sign for the velocity you've calculated because the question is asking for speed, which doesn't have a direction.

2.2 The momentum before the annihilation must be equal to the momentum after it *[1 mark]*. As the total momentum before the collision is in the horizontal direction, the sum of the vertical components of the photons' momentums must be equal to zero. Therefore, as the vertical components are equal to each other, and as $\theta_1 = \theta_2$, the photons must have the same momentum *[1 mark]*.

The equation $\lambda = \dfrac{h}{p}$ shows that the wavelengths of each photon must therefore be the same, and as $E = \dfrac{hc}{\lambda}$, the energy of each photon must also be the same *[1 mark]*.

2.3 Total energy before annihilation
$= $ kinetic energy of positron + rest energies of positron and electron
$= (0.125 \times 10^3) + (2 \times 0.510999 \times 10^6)$
$= 1.022123 \times 10^6$ eV

A positron is just the antiparticle of an electron, which is why they have the same rest energy.

Convert to joules:
$1.022123 \times 1.60 \times 10^{-19} = 1.6353... \times 10^{-13}$ J

This energy is shared equally between each photon, so energy of one photon $= (1.6353... \times 10^{-13}) \div 2$
$= 8.1769... \times 10^{-14}$ J *[1 mark]*

$E = hf$, so $f = \dfrac{E}{h} = \dfrac{8.1769... \times 10^{-14}}{6.63 \times 10^{-34}}$
$= 1.2333... \times 10^{20}$
$= $ **1.23 $\times$ 10^{20} Hz (to 3 s.f.)** *[1 mark]*

3.1 E.g. When the sail reflects a photon, the initial momentum of the photon is p and its final momentum is $-p$ so the change in momentum is $\Delta p = -2p$, and therefore the increase in the momentum of the spacecraft is $2p$ *[1 mark]*. When a sail absorbs a photon, its change in momentum is $\Delta p = -p$, where p is the momentum of the incident photon. The increase in momentum of the spacecraft is therefore p because momentum is conserved *[1 mark]*. $F = \dfrac{\Delta(mv)}{\Delta t}$ where mv is equal to the momentum, p.

$F = ma$ so $ma = \dfrac{\Delta p}{\Delta t}$. If the change in momentum is larger, the acceleration of the spacecraft will be larger, hence the acceleration of the spacecraft is larger when photons are reflected than when photons are absorbed *[1 mark]*. Sail A reflects a larger percentage of photons than sail B, so the spacecraft with sail A will have a larger acceleration than the spacecraft with sail B *[1 mark]*.

3.2 The force exerted by a single photon being absorbed by the sail:

$F = \dfrac{\Delta(mv)}{\Delta t} = \dfrac{\Delta p}{\Delta t} = \dfrac{2.76 \times 10^{-27}}{1.00 \times 10^{-3}}$
$= 2.76 \times 10^{-24}$ N *[1 mark]*

The number of photons absorbed by sail B
$= $ number of incident photons $\times$ percentage of photons absorbed
$= 1.60 \times 10^{24} \times 0.12 = 1.92 \times 10^{23}$ *[1 mark]*
Total force $= $ force per photon $\times$ number of absorbed photons
$= 2.76 \times 10^{-24} \times 1.92 \times 10^{23}$
$= 0.52992 = $ **0.530 N (to 3 s.f.)** *[1 mark]*

You'd also get full marks if you worked out the total change in momentum of all the photons and divided it by 1.00 ms.

3.3 You've been given the intensity of incident light, which is the power incident per square metre, so consider 1 m^2 of the sail:
The input power per square metre is equal to 1362 W per m^2.
The useful power output over 1 m^2 is the energy transferred per second per m^2.
You know that 75 200 J are transferred per m^2 because the units given were 75 200 Jm^{-2}.
So the useful power output per m^2 is:

$P = \dfrac{\Delta W}{\Delta t} = \dfrac{E}{\Delta t} = \dfrac{75\,200}{60.0} = 1253.333...$ Jm^{-2}s^{-1} *[1 mark]*

efficiency $= \dfrac{\text{useful output power}}{\text{input power}}$

$= \dfrac{1253.333...}{1362} = 0.9202... = $ **92.0% (to 3 s.f.)** *[1 mark]*

3.4 Resolve the force of the incident photons in the X direction to get the force applied by a photon in the direction of X, F_X.

$F_X = F_{photon}\cos\theta$. The force in the direction of X halves when:

$F_X = \dfrac{1}{2}F_{photon}$

Rearrange to get:

$\dfrac{1}{2}F_{photon} = F_{photon}\cos\theta$

Divide by F_{photon}: $\dfrac{1}{2} = \cos\theta$, so $\theta = \cos^{-1}(\dfrac{1}{2}) = $ **60°** *[1 mark]*

3.5 The solar sail may be positively charged due to photons releasing electrons from the surface of the sail by the photoelectric effect *[1 mark]*. The further the solar sail is from the Sun, the lower the intensity/power of light incident on the sail, so the fewer the number of photons hitting the sail in a certain amount of time. This means fewer photoelectrons will be released, so the solar sail will have a lower positive charge and is therefore less likely to suffer damage *[1 mark]*.

4.1 The horizontal component of the velocity will remain constant because there is no air resistance.
$v_h = 30.0\cos(5.00) = 29.885...$ ms^{-1} *[1 mark]*
To calculate v_v use $v_v = u_v + at$, so first calculate t using the horizontal velocity and distance:

$v_h = \dfrac{\Delta s_h}{\Delta t}$ so $\Delta t = \dfrac{\Delta s_h}{v_h} = \dfrac{18.4}{29.885...} = 0.6156...$ s *[1 mark]*

$v_v = u_v + at = u_v + -gt$

The acceleration g is negative here because it's acting in the opposite direction to the initial vertical velocity of the ball.

$u_v = 30.0\sin(5.00)$

$v_v = 30.0\sin(5.00) + (-9.81 \times 0.6156...) = -3.425...$ ms^{-1} *[1 mark]*

Use Pythagoras' theorem to find the resultant velocity.

$v^2 = v_h^2 + v_v^2$ so $v = \sqrt{v_h^2 + v_v^2} = \sqrt{(29.855...)^2 + (3.425...)^2}$
$= 30.081... = $ **30.1 ms^{-1} (to 3 s.f.)** *[1 mark]*

4.2 Use the horizontal impulse to find the change in horizontal momentum, and therefore the change in horizontal velocity:
The following calculations take motion to the right as positive and motion to the left as negative.

$F_h\Delta t = \Delta(mv_h)$, and the mass of the ball remains constant,

so $F_h\Delta t = m\Delta v_h$

$m = 145$ g $= 0.145$ kg

$\Delta v_h = \dfrac{F_h\Delta t}{m} = \dfrac{5.08}{0.145} = 35.034...$ ms^{-1}

Calculate the initial horizontal velocity:

$u_h = u\cos\theta_2 = 28.6\cos(35.0) = 23.427...$ ms^{-1}

So $v_h = 23.427... - 35.034...$ *[1 mark]* $= -11.606...$ ms^{-1} *[1 mark]*

The ball is initially moving to the right, but bounces off the wall and moves to the left. This means that the change in velocity (35.034... ms^{-1}) is negative because the ball has changed direction.

Answers

The final horizontal velocity, $v_h = v\cos\theta_3$,

so $v = \dfrac{v_h}{\cos\theta_3} = \dfrac{-11.606...}{\cos(48.2)} = -17.413...$

So the final speed = **17.4 ms⁻¹ (to 3 s.f.) [1 mark]**

You can ignore the final minus sign, as this indicates the direction of the velocity, but the question is asking for the speed.

4.3 First calculate the horizontal component of the force acting on the baseball as it collides with the wall:

Impulse = $F\Delta t$ so $F = \dfrac{\text{impulse}}{\Delta t} = \dfrac{5.08}{1.8 \times 10^{-3}}$

$\qquad = 2822.22...$ N **[1 mark]**

Then calculate the horizontal compression of the ball:

$F = k\Delta L$ so $\Delta L = \dfrac{F}{k} = \dfrac{2822.22...}{1.03 \times 10^5} = 0.02740...$ m **[1 mark]**

This is 35% of the baseball's diameter, so diameter of baseball is:

$0.02740... \times \dfrac{100}{35} = 0.07828...$ m

Volume of baseball = $\dfrac{4}{3}\pi r^3 = \dfrac{4}{3} \times \pi \times (0.07828... \div 2)^3$

$\qquad = 2.5122... \times 10^{-4}$ m³ **[1 mark]**

Then calculate the density:

$\rho = \dfrac{m}{V} = \dfrac{0.145}{2.5122... \times 10^{-4}} = 577.18...$

$\qquad = $ **580 kgm⁻³ (to 2 s.f.) [1 mark]**

4.4 When the ball rolls down the roof, the ball's gravitational potential energy (GPE) is transferred to kinetic energy (KE).

Energy is conserved, so the change in GPE between the top and bottom of the roof equals the balls final KE:

$\dfrac{1}{2}mv^2 = mg\Delta h$ and the mass remains constant so:

$\dfrac{1}{2}v^2 = g\Delta h$, so $v = \sqrt{2g\Delta h} = \sqrt{2 \times 9.81 \times (6.50 - 5.40)}$

$\qquad = 4.645...$ ms⁻¹ **[1 mark]**

Find the horizontal component of the initial velocity when the ball leaves the roof:

$v_h = v\cos\theta_4 = 4.645... \times \cos(32.5) = 3.918...$ ms⁻¹ **[1 mark]**

$v = \dfrac{\Delta s}{\Delta t}$ so $\Delta s_h = v_h\Delta t = 3.918... \times 0.812$

$\qquad = 3.181... = $ **3.18 m (to 3 s.f.) [1 mark]**

5.1 As the temperature of the oven decreases, the resistance of the thermistor increases **[1 mark]**. This means the thermistor gets a larger share of the potential difference and therefore the motor gets a larger share of the potential difference, which will cause the door to unlock when the p.d. across the motor is great enough **[1 mark]**.

5.2 When the temperature is 56 °C, the resistance of the thermistor is 1.6 Ω. First calculate the total resistance (R_2) of the motor (R_M) and thermistor (R_T) in parallel:

$\dfrac{1}{R_2} = \dfrac{1}{R_M} + \dfrac{1}{R_T} = \dfrac{1}{6.4} + \dfrac{1}{1.6} = 0.78125$

$R_2 = 1 \div 0.78125 = 1.28$ Ω **[1 mark]**

Now calculate the total resistance of the circuit:

The resistor and the combined resistance of the motor and thermistor are in series, $R_{total} = R_1 + R_2 = 4.0 + 1.28$

$\qquad = 5.28$ Ω **[1 mark]**

$\varepsilon = I(R + r) = 4.6 \times (5.28 + 0.85)$

$\qquad = 28.198... = $ **28 V (to 2 s.f.) [1 mark]**

5.3 $E = \dfrac{1}{2}F\Delta L$ and $F = k\Delta L$:

$E = \dfrac{1}{2}k(\Delta L)^2$, so calculate the total extension of the spring first:

To calculate the extension of the spring when the bolt is accelerating, consider the forces acting on the bolt:

E.g.

resultant force = ma

$F_{spring} - mg = ma$ and $F_{spring} = k\Delta L$, so:

$k\Delta L - mg = ma$ **[1 mark]**

$\Delta L = \dfrac{mg + ma}{k} = \dfrac{m(g + a)}{k}$

$\qquad = \dfrac{0.540 \times (9.81 + 0.142)}{855}$

$\qquad = 6.285... \times 10^{-3}$ m **[1 mark]**

$E = \dfrac{1}{2}k(\Delta L)^2 = \dfrac{1}{2} \times 855 \times (6.285... \times 10^{-3})^2$

$\qquad = 0.01688... = $ **0.0169 J (to 3 s.f.) [1 mark]**

6.1 $hf = \phi + E_{k(max)}$ so first determine the work function, ϕ.

The work function is the minimum energy needed to release electrons from the photoelectric material. Figure 11 shows that this happens at 320 nm **[1 mark]**.

$E = \dfrac{hc}{\lambda}$, so $\phi = \dfrac{hc}{\lambda} = \dfrac{6.63 \times 10^{-34} \times 3.00 \times 10^8}{320 \times 10^{-9}}$

$\qquad = 6.215... \times 10^{-19}$ J **[1 mark]**

Now calculate the kinetic energy of photoelectrons when a laser of 255 nm is shone onto the photocathode:

$hf = \phi + E_{k(max)}$, so: $E_{k(max)} = hf - \phi = \dfrac{hc}{\lambda} - \phi$

$E_{k(max)} = \dfrac{6.63 \times 10^{-34} \times 3.00 \times 10^8}{255 \times 10^{-9}} - 6.215... \times 10^{-19}$

$\qquad = 1.584... \times 10^{-19}$ J **[1 mark]**

$E_{k(max)} = \dfrac{1}{2}mv_{max}^2$

so $v_{max} = \sqrt{\dfrac{2 \times E_{k(max)}}{m}} = \sqrt{\dfrac{2 \times 1.584... \times 10^{-19}}{9.11 \times 10^{-31}}}$

$\qquad = 5.897... \times 10^5$

$\qquad = $ **5.90 × 10⁵ ms⁻¹ (to 3 s.f.) [1 mark]**

6.2 The value at which the current drops to zero lies somewhere between 280 and 320 nm. The wavelength at which the current drops to zero was used to calculate ϕ and v, so the answer to 6.1 may not be accurate **[1 mark]**. The accuracy could be improved by repeating the experiment for smaller intervals between 280 and 320 nm to find a more accurate value for the wavelength when the current drops to zero **[1 mark]**.

6.3 E.g.

Wavelength / nm

[1 mark for all non-zero values of current being higher than the original graph, 1 mark for the current dropping to zero at the same wavelength as the original graph]

6.4 $R = V \div I$, so first calculate the current.

$I = \dfrac{\Delta Q}{\Delta t}$ where ΔQ is the total charge. Each incident photon releases 1 electron and each released electron has a charge of e, so the total charge = number of photons $\times e$

$I = \dfrac{\text{number of photons} \times e}{\Delta t}$

$\quad = \dfrac{2.55 \times 10^{20} \times 1.60 \times 10^{-19}}{10.0} = 4.08$ A **[1 mark]**

$R = V \div I = 2.40 \div 4.08 = 0.5882... = $ **0.588 Ω (to 3 s.f.) [1 mark]**

6.5 $d\sin\theta = n\lambda$ and the wavelength and slit spacing are both constant.

Rearrange: $\dfrac{\lambda}{d} = \dfrac{\sin\theta}{n} = $ constant **[1 mark]**

so $\dfrac{\sin\theta_1}{1} = \dfrac{\sin\theta_2}{2}$, so $\theta_2 = \sin^{-1}(2 \times \sin\theta_1)$

$\qquad = \sin^{-1}(2 \times \sin(15.8)) = 32.994...$

$\qquad = $ **33.0° (to 3 s.f.) [1 mark]**

Specification Map

This specification map tells you where each bit of the AQA specification is covered in the book.

3.1 — Measurements and their errors

3.1.1 — Use of SI units and their prefixes
covered throughout the book

3.1.2 — Limitation of physical measurements
p.99-101, p.103

3.1.3 — Estimation of physical quantities
covered throughout the book

3.2 — Particles and radiation

3.2.1 — Particles

3.2.1.1	p.2, p.3
3.2.1.2	p.4, p.5
3.2.1.3	p.6, p.7
3.2.1.4	p.8, p.9
3.2.1.5	p.8, p.10-15
3.2.1.6	p.13, p.14

3.2.1.7	p.14

3.2.2 — Electromagnetic radiation and quantum phenomena

3.2.2.1	p.16, p.17
3.2.2.2	p.18
3.2.2.3	p.18, p.19
3.2.2.4	p.20, p.21

3.3 — Waves

3.3.1 — Progressive and stationary waves

3.3.1.1	p.24, p.25
3.3.1.2	p.25-27
3.3.1.3	p.30, p.31

3.3.2 — Refraction, diffraction and interference

3.3.2.1	p.29, p.32, p.34, p.35
3.3.2.2	p.32, p.33, p.36, p.37
3.3.2.3	p.38, p.39

3.4 — Mechanics and materials

3.4.1 — Force, energy and momentum

3.4.1.1	p.42-45
3.4.1.2	p.46-49
3.4.1.3	p.50-57
3.4.1.4	p.58, p.59, p.62, p.63
3.4.1.5	p.60, p.61

3.4.1.6	p.64, p.65
3.4.1.7	p.66-68
3.4.1.8	p.68, p.69

3.4.2 — Materials

3.4.2.1	p.68, p.70-73, p.76, p.77
3.4.2.2	p.74, p.75

3.5 — Electricity

3.5.1 — Current electricity

3.5.1.1	p.82
3.5.1.2	p.82-85
3.5.1.3	p.85-87

3.5.1.4	p.88-90, p.92, p.93
3.5.1.5	p.94, p.95
3.5.1.6	p.90, p.91

Index

Index

Index